INTRODUCTION TO GEOMETRICAL TRANSFORMATIONS

THE PRINDLE, WEBER & SCHMIDT
COMPLEMENTARY SERIES IN MATHEMATICS

Under the consulting editorship of

HOWARD W. EVES

The University of Maine

Introduction to
Geometrical Transformations

EDWARD H. BARRY

VOLUME THREE

PRINDLE, WEBER & SCHMIDT, INCORPORATED

Boston, Massachusetts

Dedicated to the memory of

the late

Julian Lowell Coolidge,

Professor of Mathematics at Harvard University,

under whose inspired instruction

the author learned that there is beauty in mathematics

Foreword

It is a pleasure to present, as one of the first volumes in the Prindle, Weber and Schmidt Complementary Series in Mathematics, this entertaining monograph by Edward H. Barry. The work can be appreciated by a very wide class of readers (any good high school geometry student can read it understandingly) and the author has lovingly and sympathetically assembled the material.

The two most significant, fruitful, and general concepts that can be introduced in an elementary course in geometry are the idea of a deductive chain of geometric statements and the idea of a geometric transformation. The former leads to the axiomatic foundation of geometry and the latter to the group-theoretic foundation of geometry. The basic purpose of Edward Barry's book is to start the reader on the second of these foundational avenues—a road that leads to Klein's famous "Erlanger Programm" and thence to many fields of current interest and research in geometry. While starting the reader down this second avenue, the author points out some of the beautiful classical scenery in the surrounding landscape of elementary geometry.

HOWARD EVES

Preface

This volume is designed to introduce the reader to certain basic concepts of elementary geometry (namely, the power of a point with respect to a circle, the radical axis of a pair of circles, families of coaxal circles, poles and polars referred to a conic section, cross ratios of point ranges and line pencils, and the principle of duality of geometrical elements), all of which lead to the procedures involved in the three important elementary transformations of circular inversion, central projection, and polar reciprocation. Some exercises have been included to give the reader practice in the application of the principles discussed.

It is hoped that the work can be used for a short course in advanced elementary geometry (often called "college geometry") or as supplementary material to a more extended course of this nature. It contains matter that every high school teacher of geometry should know, and hence the book can perhaps serve in the course offerings of Colleges of Education and of Teachers Summer Institutes. The work may also be used to introduce an interested high school student of geometry to further significant material in the field of elementary geometry. From this last point of view, a teacher of high school geometry might like to have this book in his own personal library.

EDWARD H. BARRY

Contents

CHAPTER FOUR.   CONIC SECTIONS

CHAPTER FIVE.   CENTRAL PROJECTION

CHAPTER SIX.   THEOREMS OF PASCAL
AND BRIANCHON

CHAPTER SEVEN.   THE PRINCIPLE OF DUALITY

CHAPTER EIGHT.   POLAR RECIPROCATION

Introduction

The classical, or Euclidean, method of analyzing geometrical figures treats each case as a separate problem and derives the properties of a figure through the application of logic, based on fundamental axioms. The Euclidean method is concerned largely with the metrical properties of figures, such as similarity, equality of angles, areas of figures, ratios between line segments, and so on.

During the seventeenth, eighteenth, and nineteenth centuries mathematicians modified the classical approach to geometry. Their object was to classify individual theorems into groups in which all of the members had one or more properties in common. Their methods depended on certain transformations, in the course of which an original figure becomes distorted into one which at first glance seems quite different from the first. It was discovered, however, that after a transformation, certain fundamental properties of the figure remained unchanged. These properties are known as *invariants* under the given transformation.

When the invariant characteristics are known, properties of the transformed figure may be inferred from the known properties of the original figure. Generally speaking, metrical properties are changed by a transformation. In some cases angles remain unchanged, although their sense may be reversed.

A simple example of a transformation is the casting of a shadow. Although the shadow may be a gross distortion of the object, the image will usually retain a sufficient number of the characteristics of the object

1

to permit it to be recognized. Other examples are reflections in plane or curved mirrors, perspective drawing, photography, and map projection.

Three types of transformation will be discussed herein, namely circular inversion, central projection, and polar reciprocation. Only plane figures will be considered, but at times two or more figures may lie in different planes. The treatment will not be exhaustive, but it is the author's hope that the development will be sufficient to excite the reader's interest and induce him to delve further into a fascinating field.

The first two chapters (Coaxal Circles and Cross Ratio) introduce concepts which may be new to the reader. They are included because of their importance in transformational geometry and will serve as useful references in later chapters.

Throughout the book the *sense* of line segments will be taken into account. Thus, if a segment AB is considered as positive in the direction from A to B, then the direction from B to A is to be regarded as negative. The addition or subtraction of line segments is to be made algebraically. For example, if two points A and B on a line are separated by a point C lying between them, then the expression $AB + BC$ means that we move from A to B and then back to C. The result of the two moves leaves the segment AC, measured in the direction from A to C. An equivalent result is expressed by $AB - CB$. Either direction along the line may be considered as positive.

The usual high school course in plane geometry is sufficient preparation for an understanding of the subject matter. A knowledge of trigonometry is not required, except for an understanding of the meaning of the sine function.

CHAPTER ONE

Coaxal Circles

1. The *power* of a point, with respect to a circle, is defined as the square of its distance from the center diminished by the square of the radius. In Figure 1, in which point P is outside both circles, its power with respect to circle R is $\overline{PC^2} - \overline{CA^2}$; i.e., it is the square of the tangent PA. Similarly, the power of P with respect to circle S is PB^2. In the figure P is so placed that it has the same power with respect to both circles; hence $PA = PB$. The locus of a point having this property is called the *radical axis* of the two circles. We shall show presently that the radical axis of a pair of circles is a straight line perpendicular to the line of centers.

When a point lies on a circle, its power is zero; when it lies within

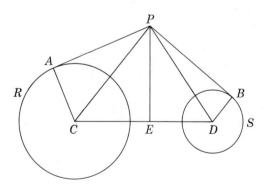

Figure 1

a circle, its power is negative and equal to the square of one-half the minimum chord drawn through the point. (The minimum chord is perpendicular to the radius through the point.) In Figure 2 the power of P with respect to circle R is $-PA^2$; with respect to circle S, its power is $-PB^2$. (Points A and B are at the extremities of the respective minimum chords through P.) P is so located in the figure that its power is the same with respect to both circles; i.e., $PA = PB$. Now, we know from elementary geometry that the common chord of two intersecting circles has the following properties:

a. It is perpendicular to the line of centers.
b. Tangents to the two circles, drawn from any point on its extension, are of equal length.
c. The minimum chords of the two circles, drawn through any point on that portion of it which lies within the circles, are of equal length.

Every point, then, on the common chord has equal power with respect to both circles. The common chord is therefore their radical axis.

It remains to prove that the radical axis of two nonintersecting circles is a straight line perpendicular to the line of centers. Refer again to Figure 1. Point P is assumed to be any point on the radical axis of circles R and S. PE is a straight line drawn perpendicular to CD. Now, since P has the same power with respect to both circles,

$$PC^2 - CA^2 = PD^2 - DB^2.$$

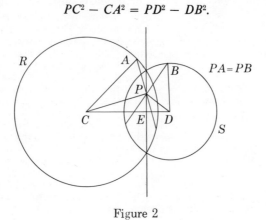

Figure 2

Using the Pythagorean Theorem, we see that this expression is equivalent to $PE^2 + CE^2 - CA^2 = PE^2 + ED^2 - DB^2$. Hence

$$CE^2 - ED^2 = CA^2 - DB^2,$$

or
$$(CE + ED)(CE - ED) = CA^2 - DB^2,$$

or
$$CD(CE - ED) = CA^2 - DB^2.$$

The last expression shows that the location of the foot of the perpendicular dropped from a point on the radical axis to the line of centers depends only on the distance between the centers of the circles and the lengths of their radii. By reversing the foregoing reasoning, it follows that every point on the perpendicular to CD at point E is on the radical axis. The proof applies to any two circles (except concentric circles), regardless of their relative positions, even when one lies wholly within the other. By definition, the radical axis of two concentric circles is the *line at infinity*.* The radical axis of two tangent circles is their common tangent at the point of tangency.

---

* "Infinity," as used in modern geometry, is an idealized region having no physical existence. Lines and points at infinity have ascribed to them ideal properties which permit the elimination of exceptions to general statements. For example, in the finite realm two parallel lines never intersect, however far they are extended. On the other hand, all other pairs of lines in the same plane intersect in a single point. The concept of infinity makes possible the general statement that every pair of lines in the plane has a single point of intersection. If the lines are parallel, they are said to intersect in a point at infinity. Similarly, two planes intersect in a straight line, except when they are parallel. The exception is removed if we assume that parallel planes intersect in a straight line lying wholly at infinity, called *the line at infinity*. To be consistent, we must agree that any other line in the plane intersects the line at infinity in a single infinite point, regardless of the direction taken along the line. We must also agree that all planes parallel to each other intersect in their common line at infinity, regardless of the direction taken on the planes. It follows that all points at infinity in a plane lie on the line at infinity in that plane.

In Chapter III, Circular Inversion, we adopt a different concept of infinity, namely that "infinity" in a given plane is a region consisting of a single point! Since we are dealing with a figment of the imagination, we are justified in inventing extraordinary properties of the region insofar as they are convenient to our purpose and consistent with properties of the finite realm.

2.   Since tangents to two circles from a point on their radical axis are of equal length, the midpoints of a pair of external common tangents lie on the radical axis, and the latter is the line joining these points. Similarly, the midpoints of the internal common tangents of a pair of nonintersecting circles lie on their radical axis.

3.   A system of circles of which any pair has the same radical axis constitutes a *coaxal family*. If two of the circles intersect, all circles of the family intersect in the same two points. Similarly, if two of the circles are tangent to each other, all members of the family are mutually tangent at the same point; and if two of the circles do not intersect, none of the circles intersects any other. Thus there are several types of coaxal families. Figures 3a, 3b, 3c, and 3d illustrate eight types. Each figure shows two related families (see Article 6). The significance of the radiating lines in Figure 3c and the two sets of parallel lines in Figure 3d will be explained in Chapter III, Circular Inversion.

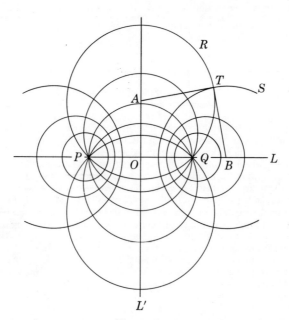

Figure 3a

4.   In Figure 3a points P and Q are common to the family of intersecting circles having line L as their radical axis. The two points are also
significant in relation to the second family of nonintersecting circles,
having L' as their axis. They are called the *limiting points* of that family,
since the center of no circle of the family can lie between the two points.
This fact becomes clear if we note that in Figure 3a the power of O is
equal to $OP^2 (= OQ^2)$, with respect to all circles of the nonintersecting
family. Hence, in the case of a circle whose center lies within the interval
PQ, the power of O with respect to it would be less than OP^2. Therefore
the circle could not be a member of the family. The limiting points can
be considered as member circles of zero radius (null circles).

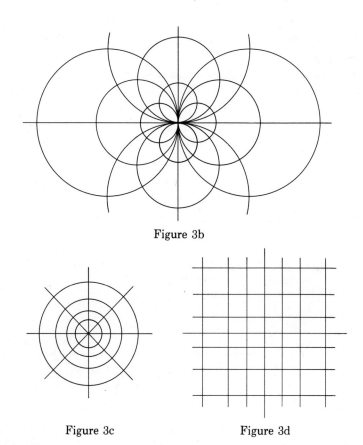

Figure 3b

Figure 3c   Figure 3d

5.   Three arbitrary circles constitute three pairs. There are therefore three radical axes. The three axes intersect in a common point,
called the *radical center*. (If the axes are parallel, the radical center lies
at infinity.) This is easily proved by noting that the point of intersection
of two of the axes has equal power with respect to all three circles. It
therefore lies on the third axis. If two circles are intersected by a third
circle, their common chords meet at the radical center. This fact provides
a convenient method for constructing the radical axis of two circles.
Refer to Figure 4. Let S and T be the two given circles. Construct an
auxiliary circle, R, intersecting both of them. The two common chords,
AB and CD, intersect at P, the radical center of circles R, S, and T.
Similarly, a second auxiliary circle, Q, determines a second point, V, the
radical center of circles Q, S, and T. Since points P and V both lie on the
radical axis of circles S and T, that axis is the line joining these points.

6.   Now refer to Figure 5, which represents a coaxal system of
nonintersecting circles. F is the line of centers; L is the common radical
axis; P and Q are the limiting points. The dashed circle has PQ as a
diameter. O is the center of the system, the intersection of lines F and L.
Since O is on the radical axis, the length of the tangent from O to all
circles, including the null circles, is constant and equal to the radius OQ
of the dashed circle. Therefore the dashed circle is the locus of points of
tangency of tangents from O to all circles of the system. Since a tangent
to a circle is perpendicular to a radius through the point of tangency,

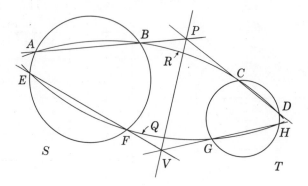

Figure 4

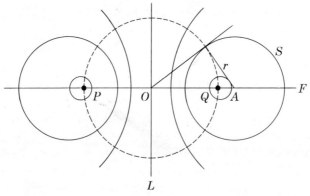

Figure 5

as illustrated by a typical circle S in the figure, it follows that the dashed circle cuts all circles of the system orthogonally (at right angles.) The dashed circle is one member of a second coaxal family having the limiting points P and Q as their common points of intersection. Each circle of the second family is also orthogonal to all circles of the first family. This will be clear by referring again to Figure 3a, in which circles R and S are arbitrary members of the respective families. A is the center of R, and B is the center of S. Since A lies on the radical axis of the nonintersecting family, the length AT of the tangent to S must equal AQ, the radius of R. Accordingly, the radius of R at the point T, being tangent to S, is perpendicular to the radius of S at point T. Two families of coaxal circles which intersect each other orthogonally are known as *conjugate* coaxal families.

The foregoing is intended only as an introduction to coaxal circles. They will be considered further in Chapter III, *Circular Inversion.*

CHAPTER TWO

Cross Ratio

7.   When two or more straight lines pass through a common point, they are said to be concurrent. The group of lines is known as a *pencil*. Similarly, when several points lie on a straight line, they are collinear. The group of points is called a *range*. *Cross ratio* (sometimes called *anharmonic ratio*) has to do with the relationship among the line segments set off by four points of a range. Cross ratio has a definite numerical value with respect to a given pencil or range. Its value, however, depends on the order in which the members are taken. Refer to Figure 6, which shows a range of the points A, B, C, and D. The line segment between any two of these points may be considered as being divided by the other two points. Take segment AB, for instance. Point C divides it in the ratio CA/CB. This is called internal division, because C lies between A and B. Point D, on the other hand, divides AB externally in the ratio DA/DB. Suppose we consider distances measured in one direction as positive, and distances measured in the other direction as negative. It is apparent that CA/CB has a negative value, whereas DA/DB is positive. Cross ratio is defined as the ratio between these two ratios. It is represented symbolically as $(ABCD)$. Note that the order of the letters is significant. $(ABCD)$ expresses the value of the cross ratio

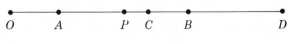

Figure 6

11

of the four points when the segment AB is divided by the points C and D. Specifically,

$$(ABCD) = \frac{\dfrac{CA}{CB}}{\dfrac{DA}{DB}}.$$

Still referring to Figure 6, if we consider that the segment CD is divided by the points B and A, the cross ratio would be expressed as

$$(CDBA) = \frac{\dfrac{BC}{BD}}{\dfrac{AC}{AD}}.$$

8.   A range of four points may be represented by twenty-four different orders of its members, the number of permutations of four objects taken four at a time. Accordingly, there are twenty-four ways of expressing the cross ratio of the range. However, not all lead to different numerical values. It will be shown presently that there are at most only six different values of the cross ratio of a given range, the other eighteen being duplications.

9.   When two points divide a line segment internally and externally in the same ratio, the division is said to be *harmonic*. The value of the cross ratio is then equal to -1. The range is also called harmonic. Thus the expression $(ADBC) = -1$ describes a harmonic range in which points B and C divide the segment AD internally and externally in the same ratio.

10.   Referring to Figure 6, suppose that the segment AB is divided harmonically by points C and D; i.e., $CA/CB = -(DA/DB)$. Also suppose that P is the midpoint of AB. We shall prove that PB is a mean

proportional between PC and PD; i.e., $PC \times PD = PB^2$. For if we let $PB = b$, $PC = c$, and $PD = d$, then $AP = b$. Now, since

$$\frac{-c-b}{b-c} = -\frac{-d-b}{-d+b}, \frac{b+c}{b-c} = -\frac{d+b}{b-d}.$$

Multiplying out, we have $b^2 - bd + bc - cd = -bd - b^2 + cd + bc$, or $2b^2 = 2cd$, or $PB^2 = PC \times PD$. By reversing these steps, it is clear that if $PB^2 = PC \times PD$, then C and D divide the segment AB harmonically. C and D are called *harmonic conjugates* with respect to A and B.

11. The importance of cross ratio lies in the fact that it is an *invariant* characteristic of a figure under certain types of transformation, notably *central projection*, of which perspective drawing, photography, and aerial mapping are examples. The numerical value of the cross ratio is seldom of importance, except when it is equal to -1, which indicates that the ratio is harmonic.

12. An interesting relationship exists among the six basic values of the cross ratio of a given range. The expression $(ABCD) = k$ is equivalent to

$$\frac{\dfrac{CA}{CB}}{\dfrac{DA}{DB}} = k.$$

This can be rewritten as $CA/CB \times DB/DA = k$. Obviously, the value is not changed if we interchange the two fractions; thus

$$DB/DA \times CA/CB = k.$$

This is equivalent to

$$\frac{\dfrac{DB}{DA}}{\dfrac{CB}{CA}} = k \quad \text{or} \quad (BADC) = k.$$

Thus a simultaneous reversal of the first two and the last two points does not change the value of the cross ratio. The value changes, however, when the order of only one pair of points is reversed. Let us examine the effect of reversing the first two points, remembering that the basic expression

$$(ABCD) = \frac{\dfrac{CA}{CB}}{\dfrac{DA}{DB}} = \frac{CA}{CB} \times \frac{DB}{DA} = k.$$

Now,

$$(BACD) = \frac{\dfrac{CB}{CA}}{\dfrac{DB}{DA}} = \frac{CB}{CA} \times \frac{DA}{DB} = \frac{1}{k}.$$

We would arrive at the same result by reversing the third and fourth points.

To determine the effect of reversing the second and third points, we need to use a fundamental relationship among the segments set off by four points, $ABCD$, on a range, namely

$$AB \times DC + AC \times BD + AD \times CB = 0.$$

(Refer to Figure 6.) This may be verified by writing this equation in its equivalent form:

$$AB(DA - CA) + AC(AD - AB) - DA(AB - AC) = 0.$$

Multiplying out, we have

$$AB \times DA - AB \times CA +$$

$$AC \times AD - AC \times AB - DA \times AB + DA \times AC = 0.$$

It is evident that the left-hand side of the equation vanishes. Returning now to the equation $AB \times DC + AC \times BD + AD \times CB = 0$, we divide both sides by $AD \times CB$. We then have

$$\frac{AB \times DC}{AD \times CB} + \frac{AC \times BD}{AD \times CB} + 1 = 0.$$

This is equivalent to

$$-\frac{\dfrac{BA}{BC}}{\dfrac{DA}{DC}} - \frac{\dfrac{CA}{CB}}{\dfrac{DA}{DB}} + 1 = 0.$$

Hence

$$\frac{\dfrac{BA}{BC}}{\dfrac{DA}{DC}} = 1 - \frac{\dfrac{CA}{CB}}{\dfrac{DA}{DB}}.$$

The latter expression states that $(ACBD) = 1 - (ABCD)$. In other words, if $(ABCD) = k$, then $(ACBD) = 1 - k$.

We now have three expressions for the cross ratio of the range of Figure 6, namely k, $1/k$, and $1 - k$. As an exercise, the reader may wish to experiment with further interchanges of the points. He will find that there are a total of six different ways to express the cross ratio, namely k, $1/k$, $1 - k$, $1/(1 - k)$, $(k - 1)/k$, and $k/(k - 1)$. Other interchanges of the points produce duplications of these.

It remains to investigate the value of the cross ratio of a range of four points when one of them is at infinity. Referring to Figure 6, assume that points A, B, and C remain fixed and that D moves out to the right along the line. For each position of D there is a different value for the cross ratio, but the ratio CA/CB does not change. As D recedes indefinitely, the ratio DA/DB approaches unity as a limit. Consequently, at the limit the cross ratio $(ABC\infty) = CA/CB$. If C is the midpoint of the segment AB, then $(ABC\infty) = -1$, and the range is harmonic. Thus, if a line segment is bisected by a point, the three points plus the point at infinity on the line constitute a harmonic range.

We are now prepared to investigate the first of three types of geometrical transformations.

CHAPTER THREE

Circular Inversion

13. Figure 7 illustrates the basic definition of *circular inversion*. We start with a fixed circle C, with center O and radius r. C is called the *circle of inversion*; O the *origin*, or *center of inversion*. P is any point in the plane of the circle, either inside or outside the circle. By definition, the inverse of P (with respect to the circle) is another point on the line OP, whose distance from O is equal to r^2/OP. In the figure P' is the inverse of P. P is also the inverse of P'. Inversion gets its name from the fact that as P moves, OP' is inversely proportional to OP. The inverse of a point outside the circle is a point inside, and vice versa. Obviously, every finite point in the plane has an inverse. To be consistent and thus avoid exceptions, all points infinitely distant from the origin are considered to be concentrated at a single point, called *the point at infinity*,

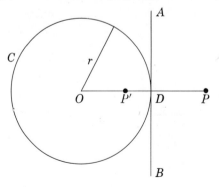

Figure 7

17

which is the inverse of the origin. If P lies on the circle of inversion, it inverts into itself, for in that case $OP = r$, and, by the basic definition,

$$OP' = \frac{r^2}{OP} = \frac{r^2}{r} = r.$$

14. If P is a moving point, its inverse P' traces out a path which is the inverse of the path traced by P. Thus every curve has its inverse. Our object is to determine the relationship between certain curves and their inverses; but first we shall consider two methods of constructing the inverse of a point. Figure 8 illustrates the first method. If P is a point outside the circle of inversion, we draw two tangents to the circle from P and also draw the line OP. A and B are the points of tangency and AB is the chord of contact. We know from elementary geometry that the lines AB and OP are perpendicular. Let P' be their point of intersection. Now, P and P' are mutually inverse with respect to circle C, for triangles OAP and $AP'O$ are similar (corresponding angles are equal); therefore $OP'/r = r/OP$, or $OP \times OP' = r^2$. If P lies inside the circle, we draw the minimum chord through P and the tangents at its extremities. These tangents intersect at the inverse of P. The proof is obvious. (For future reference we note that in Figure 8 the line AB is called the *polar* of point P. Its significance will be explained in Chapter VIII, Polar Reciprocation.)

The second method of inverting a point is illustrated by Figure 9. This construction can be performed by using only a pair of compasses. With P as center and radius PO, swing an arc intersecting C in points D

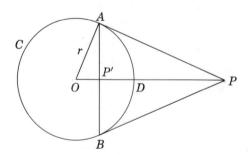

Figure 8

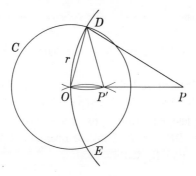

Figure 9

and E. With D and E as centers and radius OD, swing arcs intersecting at P'. Then P' is the inverse of P, for triangle ODP' is isosceles and similar to triangle OPD; hence $OP'/r = r/OP$, or $OP \times OP' = r^2$. Note that this construction presupposes that the distance OP is such that an arc drawn with P as center and radius OP will intersect circle C. When this is not the case, we employ a modification of the method, which will be explained later (Article 28).

From the definition of inversion it is apparent that the unlimited line OP inverts into itself, points lying outside the circle of inversion exchanging places with points inside. A circle concentric with O inverts into another circle concentric with O, their radii being in inverse ratio.

15. It is to be noted that r, the radius of inversion, merely determines the scale of the inverted figure.* It is of interest, therefore, to determine the effect of inverting a point with respect to a circle of infinite radius, namely a straight line. Referring again to Figure 7, we note that

$$OP = r + DP, \text{ and } OP' = r - P'D. \text{ Now, since } OP \times OP' = r^2,$$

$$(r + DP) \times (r - P'D) = r^2.$$

---

* The circle of inversion is seldom of importance. We shall frequently refer to inversion with respect to a point as origin, and omit mention of the circle of inversion.

Expanding, we have

$$r^2 + rDP - rP'D - DP \times P'D = r^2, \text{ or } DP - P'D = DP \times P'D/r.$$

Now, if we hold D fixed and allow O to move indefinitely toward the left, as r becomes infinite circle C approaches the line AB and the right-hand side of the last equation approaches zero (since $P'D$ remains finite). At the limit, $DP = P'D$. Thus the inverse of a point with respect to a straight line is its reflected image.

16.   We are now prepared to determine the inverse of a straight line which does not pass through the origin. Refer to Figure 10, where we are given line L and point O, the center of inversion. Let P be the foot of a perpendicular from O to L; also, let P' be the inverse of P. Take any other point Q on L, draw OQ, and let Q' be the inverse of Q. Now consider the triangles $OP'Q'$ and OPQ. We know that

$$OP \times OP' = OQ \times OQ' = r^2.$$

Hence $OP/OQ' = OQ/OP'$. Therefore the triangles are similar, since they have an angle in common and corresponding sides in proportion. Since angle OPQ is a right angle, it follows that angle $OQ'P'$ is also a right angle. Now, the position of Q on L is arbitrary; accordingly, regardless of its position, angle $OQ'P'$ is always a right angle. Therefore,

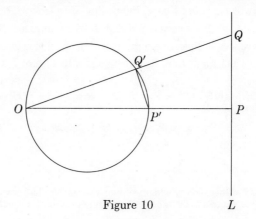

Figure 10   L

as Q moves along L, its inverse Q' describes a circle passing through O and having OP' as a diameter. Therefore the inverse of a straight line is a circle through the origin. The converse is also true: the inverse of a circle through the origin is a straight line perpendicular to the diameter through the origin. The proof is obvious.

17. We shall next determine the inverse of a circle which does not pass through the origin. Refer to Figure 11, where we are given circle S, to be inverted with respect to the origin O. Let the line from O, through the center of S, intersect S in Q and P. Then QP is a diameter of S. Let P' and Q' be the inverses, respectively, of P and Q. P' and Q' lie on the line OQP. It is evident that the inverse of S will be symmetrical about the line OQP. We therefore need to consider the inverse of only a semi-circle of S. Let R be an arbitrary point on this semicircle, and let R' be its inverse. Draw the straight lines $OR'R$, $Q'R'$, $R'P'$, QR, and RP. Now, $OP \times OP' = OQ \times OQ' = OR \times OR'$; hence $OR'/OP = OP'/OR$.

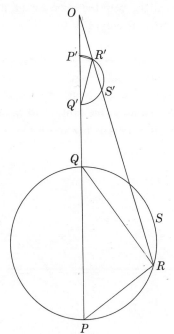

Figure 11

Triangles ORP and $OP'R'$ are therefore similar. Hence angle $OP'R' =$ angle ORP; also, angle $OQ'R' =$ angle ORQ (triangles $OQ'R'$ and OQR are similar); and, subtracting, angle $OP'R' -$ angle $OQ'R' =$ angle $ORP -$ angle $ORQ =$ a right angle. Hence, angle $P'R'Q'$ ($=$ angle $OR'Q' -$ angle $OR'P'$) $=$ a right angle. It is evident that, for all positions of R on the semicircle S, point R' will describe a path such that angle $P'R'Q'$ will always be a right angle. Consequently, the path of R' is a semicircle, with $P'Q'$ as diameter. Therefore the inverse of circle S is another circle, S'.

18.   It will now be shown that the angle between the inverses of two intersecting curves is the same as the angle between the original curves. (The angle between two curves is defined as the angle between their tangents at the point of intersection.) The method of proof will be to show that a single curve and its inverse make equal angles with a common secant from the origin. Since a second curve and its inverse will also make equal angles with the same secant, it will follow that the angle between the original curves is the same as that between their inverses.

Refer to Figure 12. Let S be the given curve, S' its inverse, and OP a secant from O. Points P and P' are mutually inverse. Take another point Q on S, close to P. Let Q', lying on OQ, be the inverse of Q. Q' lies, of course, on S'. Draw T, the tangent to S, at P, and draw t, the tangent to S', at P'. Draw chords PQ and $P'Q'$. Note that the tangents

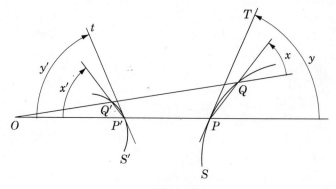

Figure 12

T and t make angles y and y', respectively, with secant $OP'P$. Note also that chord PQ intersects secant OQ at an angle x, and that chord $P'Q'$ intersects secant OP at an angle x'. Since triangles $OP'Q'$ and OPQ are similar, it follows that angle x = angle x'. Now let point Q move along S towards point P. Q' will also move towards P'. Angle x approaches angle y, the angle between the tangent T and the secant OP. Angle x' approaches the corresponding angle y'. Hence, at the limit, when Q coincides with P, angle y = angle y'. We have thus proved that a secant makes equal angles with a curve and its inverse. If another curve were now drawn through P, that curve and its inverse would make equal angles with the same secant. Since the angle between two curves is the algebraic sum of the angles they make with a common secant, it is evident that the angle between two curves is the same as the angle between their inverses, although opposite in sense.

The invariance of angularity under inversion is a remarkable and useful property, especially when the angles are right angles. For example, if two circles are orthogonal (intersect at right angles), they invert into two orthogonal circles.

19. The following is a summary of the facts about inversion which we have discussed up to this point:

a. Points invert into points.

b. A straight line through the origin inverts into itself.

c. The circle of inversion inverts into itself.

d. A straight line not through the origin inverts into a circle through the origin.

e. A circle not through the origin inverts into a circle not through the origin (unless the original circle is a straight line).

f. If one figure is the inverse of another, the other is the inverse of the first.

g. The inverse of a figure with respect to a straight line is the reflected image of the figure in the line.

h. The center of a circle and the point at infinity are mutually inverse with respect to the circle.

i. The angles between elements of a figure are invariant in amount under inversion, but opposite in sense.
j. Circles concentric with the origin invert into other circles concentric with the origin.

20.   We now investigate another remarkable property of inversion. If two points (or configurations) are mutually inverse with respect to a circle, then after inversion of the entire figure with respect to another circle, corresponding elements will be inverse to each other with respect to the inverse of the first circle; i.e., the property of inverseness is invariant under inversion.

As a first step in the proof, an important property of a circle orthogonal to the circle of inversion will be demonstrated. Refer to Figure 13. We are given circle S, orthogonal to C, the circle of inversion. Let P be one of the points of intersection of the circles. Note that, because of orthogonality, the radius of either circle at P is tangent to the other circle. Now through O draw a secant to S, intersecting the latter in A and B. From elementary geometry, $OA \times OB = r^2$; but this is also the condition that A and B be mutually inverse with respect to C. This establishes the truth of the following theorem: if a secant is drawn from the center of one of two orthogonal circles, the points of intersection of the secant with the second circle are mutually inverse with respect to the first circle. Conversely, if two points on a circle are mutually inverse with respect to a second circle, the two circles are orthogonal. (We omit the obvious proof.)

With these properties in mind, refer to Figure 14. We are given circle S and points A and B mutually inverse with respect to it. Let O

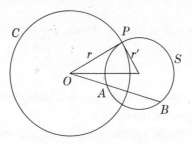

Figure 13

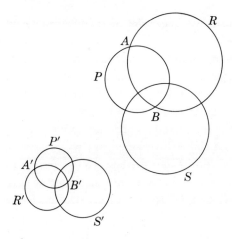

Figure 14

be the center of inversion. Draw circles P and R, each passing through A and B. Then circles P and R will each be orthogonal to circle S. Now invert the entire figure with respect to O. Circle S inverts into circle S', and circles P and R into circles P' and R', respectively. Now, since P and R are each orthogonal to S, P' and R' will each be orthogonal to S' (Article 19, Fact i). Note that since points A and B are each common to circles P and R, their inverses (with respect to O) will be the points of intersection, A' and B', of circles P' and R'. Also, by the principle developed in the preceding paragraph, there is another point on P' (corresponding to A') which is the inverse of A' with respect to S'; but A' also lies on R'; hence the inverse of A' also lies on R'. Therefore the inverse of A' (with respect to S') is common to P' and R'; i.e., it is the point B'. This proves the theorem stated at the beginning of this article.

21. The theorem just proved is a fundamental one and leads to many interesting conclusions. For example, we know that the center of a circle and the point at infinity are mutually inverse with respect to the circle. After inversion with respect to a new origin, the circle inverts into

a second circle, the point at infinity inverts into the origin, and the center of the first circle inverts into a point which is the inverse of the origin with respect to the second circle. This fact enables us to find the center of a given circle, using only a pair of compasses (not a straight-edge). Refer to Figure 15, where we are given circle S with unknown center. Take any point O on its circumference as a center of inversion. With O as center and an arbitrary radius, draw circle C, intersecting S in points A and B. Invert the figure with respect to C. Circle C is its own inverse. S inverts into the line AB (we do not draw the line). The un-known center of S inverts into the image of O reflected in the line AB. Call this point P'. It may be constructed by swinging two arcs with radius OA and centers A and B. Since P' is the inverse of the unknown center P of circle S, P may be constructed by inverting P' with respect to C. This can be done by the method of Figure 9.

It is suggested that the reader at this point review Chapters I and II.

22.   Referring to Figure 5, it will be recalled that the dashed circle is orthogonal to S, an arbitrary circle of the coaxal family. F, the line of centers, is a secant through the center of S, cutting the dashed circle in P and Q, the limiting points of the system. Consequently, the product $AP \times AQ = r^2$; but this is the condition that P and Q be mutually in-verse with respect to S. Since S is an arbitrary circle of the system, it follows that the limiting points are mutually inverse with respect to every circle of the coaxal family.

23.   Let us now invert the entire system of coaxal circles in Figure 5, using either limiting point, say P, as the center of inversion. Because

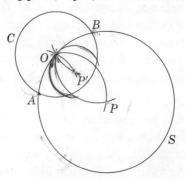

Figure 15

of the invariant property of inverseness, P and Q, which are mutually inverse with respect to every circle of the system, will invert into points which are mutually inverse with respect to the inverse of every circle; but note that P, the origin, inverts into the point at infinity. Therefore Q, the inverse of P with respect to every circle of the original system, must invert into a point which is the inverse of the point at infinity with respect to all of the inverted circles; i.e., it is the center of a system of concentric circles having the inverse of Q (with respect to P) as center.

24. Refer now to Figure 3a, which represents two conjugate systems of coaxal circles. If we invert the entire figure with respect to either limiting point, the nonintersecting circles, as we have just seen, will be transformed into concentric circles, as in Figure 3c. The system of intersecting circles of Figure 3a will be transformed into the system of radiating lines of Figure 3c. It is of interest to note that the invariance of the orthogonality of the circles of the two families in Figure 3a is maintained in the orthogonality between the straight lines and circles of Figure 3c.

Inversion of the tangent circles in Figure 3b, with respect to the point of tangency, results in the two sets of mutually orthogonal parallel lines in Figure 3d. (The circles of each system invert into lines perpendicular to the radical axis of the conjugate system. The radical axes are unchanged by the inversion.)

25. Another interesting property of inversion concerns a range of points on a straight line through the origin. The cross ratio of a range of four such points is invariable under inversion. To prove this, consider the range $ABCD$ in Figure 6, having a cross ratio $(ABCD)$. Take a point O on the line as center of inversion. We assume it to be to the left of A, but its position on the line is immaterial. Let $OA = a$, $OB = b$, $OC = c$, and $OD = d$. Now,

$$(ABCD) = \frac{\dfrac{CA}{CB}}{\dfrac{DA}{DB}} = -\frac{\left(\dfrac{c-a}{b-c}\right)}{\dfrac{-(d-a)}{-(d-b)}} = \frac{a-c}{b-c} \times \frac{d-b}{d-a}.$$

Let the inverses of A, B, C, and D be A', B', C', and D'. Also let $OA' = a'$, $OB' = b'$, $OC' = c'$, and $Od' = d'$. If r is the radius of the assumed circle of inversion, then $a' = r^2/a$, $b' = r^2/b$, $c' = r^2/c$, and $d' = r^2/d$. Now, the cross ratio of the range after inversion is

$$(A'B'C'D') = \frac{\dfrac{r^2}{a} - \dfrac{r^2}{c}}{\dfrac{r^2}{b} - \dfrac{r^2}{c}} \times \frac{\dfrac{r^2}{d} - \dfrac{r^2}{b}}{\dfrac{r^2}{d} - \dfrac{r^2}{a}}.$$

Simplifying, we have

$$\frac{\dfrac{c - a}{ac}}{\dfrac{c - b}{bc}} \times \frac{\dfrac{b - d}{bd}}{\dfrac{a - d}{ad}} = \frac{\dfrac{CA}{CB}}{\dfrac{DA}{DB}}.$$

Thus the cross ratio of the original range has been unchanged by the inversion.

26. Inversion is useful in transforming theorems. As an illustration, let us invert the elementary theorem that the three altitudes of a triangle are concurrent. Refer to Figure 16a. The inverse of this figure, referred to point H as origin, is shown in Figure 16b. A new theorem may now be deduced from the latter figure, as follows: if three circles have a point in common, then the common chord of each pair passes through the center of the third. The following reasoning is used as proof: the three altitudes, since they pass through the origin, are unchanged by the inversion. They become the lines $B'F'$, $A'E'$, and $C'G'$. The three sides of the triangle, AB, BC, and CA become the three circles S, T, and U. The points A', B', and C', in which the circles intersect, are the inverses, respectively, of the vertices A, B, and C of the triangle. Now, since altitude AE passes through A and H, its inverse $A'E'$ is the common chord of circles S and U. Similarly, the inverses of the other two altitudes are the common chords of circles S and T, and T and U. Since the altitudes are orthogonal to the sides of the triangle, the lines $B'F'$,

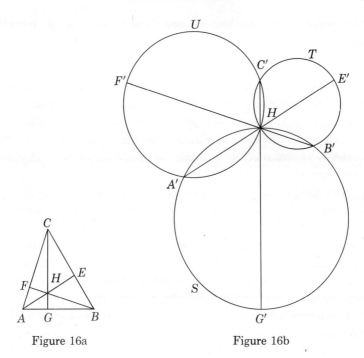

Figure 16a   Figure 16b

$A'E'$, and $C'G'$ cut the circles U, T, and S orthogonally; i.e., they are diameters of these circles.

As another example, consider the following theorem: the angle inscribed in a semicircle is a right angle. By inversion we can prove the following theorem: if two straight lines intersect at right angles, and if a circle passing through their point of intersection also passes through a fixed point on one of the lines and through a variable point on the other, then the line joining the fixed and variable points is a diameter of the circle. It is suggested that the reader draw his own figures. To illustrate the first theorem, draw circle S and a diameter OA. Take any point P on its circumference. Draw OP and AP. Then OP and AP form a right angle. Now draw the inverse figure, referred to point O as origin (take a new point O). S becomes a straight line S', not passing through O. The diameter OA becomes a straight line through O, perpendicular to S'. P', the inverse of P, becomes a point on S'. Line OP becomes the straight line joining O and P'. Line AP becomes a circle passing through

A', P', and O. Now, since lines OP and AP are at right angles, line OP' intersects the latter circle at right angles; i.e., it is a diameter.

27. Lorenzo Mascheroni (1750–1801), an Italian mathematician, discovered the following extraordinary theorem which bears his name: every construction possible with straightedge and compasses is possible with compasses alone. It is curious that the simplest proof of this theorem is by means of the principles of inversion, probably unknown to Mascheroni.

An objection may be raised to the generality of the theorem, since a straight line obviously cannot be drawn with a pair of compasses. However, as many points on the line as desired may be constructed. On the other hand, the purpose of drawing lines in geometrical constructions is usually to find their points of intersection with other lines or circular arcs in the figure. As will be shown presently, such points can always be found without the use of the straightedge.

It is impossible to analyze each of the multitude of constructions which can be performed with straightedge and compasses and to prove that each of these is possible with compasses alone. The proof of Mascheroni's theorem is more general. Since the function of the straightedge is to determine the points of intersection of a straight line with other lines or arcs, it will be sufficient to show that such points can be established, in all cases, by the intersections of circular arcs. The proof will consist of showing that all four of the following constructions, which include all possible uses of the straightedge and compasses, can be performed with compasses alone:

a. Draw a circle, given its center and radius.
b. Find the points of intersection of two circles.
c. Find the points of intersection with a given circle of the straight line connecting two given points.
d. Find the point of intersection of the straight lines joining two given pairs of points. (The lines are not given.)

Inversion provides the basis of proof that all of these fundamental constructions can be performed with compasses alone. The possibility of constructions *a* and *b* is obvious. To prove construction *c*, refer to Figure 17, where we are given circle *C*, center *O*, and the points *A* and *B*. We wish to find the points of intersection of line *AB* with circle *C*. With centers *A* and *B*, radii *AO* and *BO*, respectively, draw arcs intersecting at *P*. (*P* is the inverse of *O* in *AB*.) Now invert *P* with respect to *C* (by the method of Figure 9), giving point *Q*. With *Q* as center and radius *OQ*, draw circle *S*, cutting *C* at points *X* and *Y*. These are the required points. Circle *S* is the inverse of the line *AB*, with respect to circle *C*. Because of the invariance of inverseness, the inverses of points *O* and *P* (which are mutually inverse with respect to *AB*) will be mutually inverse with respect to the inverse of *AB*, i.e., circle *S*. But *O* inverts, with respect to *C*, into the point at infinity; and *P* inverts to *Q*, the center of circle *S* (since the center of *S* and the point at infinity are mutually inverse with respect to *S*). Therefore circle *S*, being the inverse of line *AB* with respect to *C*, has the same points of intersection with circle *C* as does line *AB*.

It remains to prove construction *d*. Refer to Figure 18, where we are given pairs of points *A*, *B* and *P*, *Q*, and, to find *X*, the point of intersection of lines *AB* and *PQ*. Draw circle *C*, with arbitrary center and radius. Label its center, *O*. By the method of the preceding paragraph, construct circles *R* and *S*, the respective inverses of *AB* and *PQ*, with respect to *C*. Their point of intersection, *Y*, will be the inverse of *X*, the

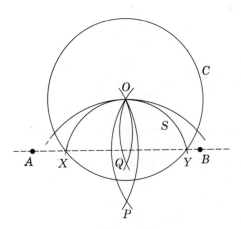

Figure 17

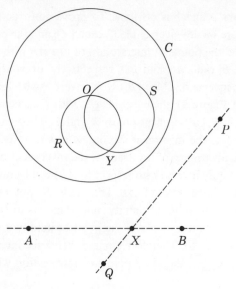

Figure 18

point of intersection of lines AB and PQ. X is found by inverting Y with respect to C.

This completes the general proof of the Mascheroni Theorem.

28. Although we know from the Mascheroni Theorem that all constructions are possible by following the successive steps of the conventional constructions employing straightedge and compasses, in many cases alternative methods are available. Several examples of these have already been given, such as the inversion of a point, illustrated by Figure 9; finding the center of a circle, Figure 15; and the constructions of Figures 17 and 18. One further example will be given.

Find the point midway between two given points and on the line joining them (the line is not given). Only a pair of compasses may be used, and the point must be established by the distinct intersection of two circular arcs, not by trial and error. It is suggested that the reader, as an exercise, attempt this construction before reading further. The solution is not easy to find.

Refer to Figure 19, where A and B are the given points. With A and B as centers and with radius AB, draw circles S and T. With the same

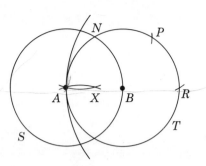

Figure 19

radius, step off three successive points on T, establishing the point R, which is evidently on AB, extended, and at a distance from A equal to $2AB$. The distance of the required point from A is $\frac{1}{2}AB$. If, now, the point R is inverted with respect to S (by the method of Figure 9), its inverse will be X, the desired midpoint of AB, since

$$AX = \frac{AB^2}{AR} = \frac{AB^2}{2AB} = \frac{AB}{2}.$$

As a corollary to this construction, note that we have constructed a segment AR which is twice the length of AB. By drawing another circle with center R and radius RB, and stepping off RB successively on its circumference, we can find another point on AB, extended, whose distance from A is $3AB$. This process can be repeated for any integral multiple of AB. The procedure provides a means for constructing the inverse of a point inside the circle of inversion when the point is too close to the origin to permit the direct application of the method of Figure 9. The way out of the dilemma is to construct an auxiliary point, n times as far from the origin as the given point, and then construct its inverse. The point so constructed will be one-nth the distance of the required point from the origin. The required point is found by multiplying the last distance by n.

29. In 1873 a French army officer, C. N. Peaucellier, invented a linkage for constructing, mechanically, a straight line. The device, called the Peaucellier Cell, is illustrated by Figure 20. It consists of

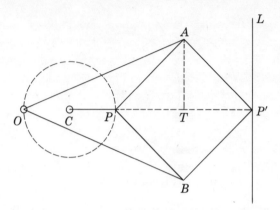

Figure 20

seven links, pivoted at points O, A, B, C, P, and P'. Points O and C are fixed to the drawing table. Points A, B, P, and P' are free to move within the limits of the device. The length of link CP is equal to the distance OC. Obviously, point P will describe a circular arc which, if extended, would pass through O. Meanwhile, point P' will describe a straight line, L. The explanation is that point P' is always the inverse of P, with respect to O. This will be apparent from the following:

$$OP = OT - PT, \; OP' = OT + TP' = OT + TP \,(\text{numerically}),$$
$$OP \times OP' = (OT - PT) \times (OT + TP) = OT^2 - TP^2$$
$$= (OA^2 - AT^2) - (AP^2 - AT^2)$$
$$= OA^2 - AP^2 = r^2 \,(\text{a constant}).$$

Thus P and P' are mutually inverse with respect to a circle with center at O and with radius r. Therefore, as P describes a circle through O, P' will trace a straight line, L, the inverse of the circle through O. The radius of inversion, r, does not appear in the figure. It is equal to the square root of $(OA^2 - AP^2)$.

It is notable that the Peaucellier Cell is a mechanism for drawing a straight line which does not require a pre-existing straight line for its construction.

If, in Figure 20, the link CP is removed, point P will be free to trace any curve. In that case, P' will trace the inverse of that curve.

30. One of the most interesting applications of inversion is in connection with a continuous chain of tangent circles, each of which is tangent externally and internally to an inner and outer circle. Two examples of such a system are shown in Figures 21a and 21b. In Figure 21a the inner and outer circles are concentric, and the circles comprising the chain are all of equal size. A suitable choice of the relative diameters of the inner and outer circles is necessary in order that the construction may be possible; but when the construction has been completed, it becomes obvious that the positions of the circles forming the chain are not fixed. The figure resembles a ball bearing in which the balls are tangent to each other and to the inner and outer races. In such a bearing, the circle of balls could be rotated without their breaking contact with each other or with the two races.

In Figure 21b the inner and outer circles are not concentric. Assuming that the relative diameters of these two circles have been properly chosen, it will be possible to construct the chain of tangent circles. It is not evident, however, that the starting point of the chain is immaterial. Yet such is the case, for Figure 21b is obtained by inverting Figure 21a, with respect to point *O*. Each circle of the latter figure inverts into a corresponding circle in Figure 21b, and tangent elements in one figure invert into tangent elements in the other. If, now, we imagine the rotation of the chain of circles in Figure 21a about the center of the figure,

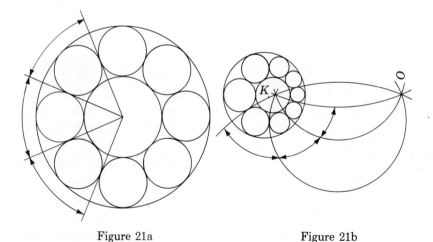

Figure 21a   Figure 21b

a curious phenomenon will occur in Figure 21b. The inner and outer circles will remain fixed, and the chain of unequal circles will rotate. The circles of the chain will expand and contract while maintaining tangency with each other and with the inner and outer circles. Thus it becomes evident that if the construction of Figure 21b is possible, the starting point for the first circle of the chain is immaterial. It is certain that there will be exactly sufficient space to accommodate the last circle of the chain.

As a further commentary on Figures 21a and 21b, we know that since one figure is the inverse of the other, the inner and outer circles of Figure 21b are members of a family of nonintersecting coaxal circles. Point K, the inverse of the origin, O, with respect to either of the two circles, is one of the limiting points; O is the other. Point K, however, is also the inverse of the center of Figure 21a, with respect to the origin O. Note the lines radiating from the center of Figure 21a and passing through the tangent points in the chain. They obviously make equal angles with each other. The inverses of these lines are, in Figure 21b, the circles which pass through the two limiting points, K and O, and the points of tangency in the chain. Accordingly, the latter circles make equal angles with each other. They are, incidentally, members of the conjugate coaxal family.

31. As a final illustration of inversion, we shall consider the famous problem of Apollonius (a mathematician of the third century B.C.). Given three circles in a plane, the problem is to construct, with straightedge and compasses, a circle tangent to the three given circles. The problem is illustrated by the solid-line circles of Figure 22a. The figure represents only one of eight possible cases, since the required circle may be tangent internally or externally to each of the three given circles. The present discussion will be confined to the case of external tangency, as illustrated by the figure.

As a preliminary to the solution of the problem, we note that if the radii of the three given circles are each increased by the same amount, and the radius of the required circle is diminished by a like amount, tangency is still maintained between the required and given circles. With this in view, we increase the radii of circles S, T, and U by one-half the

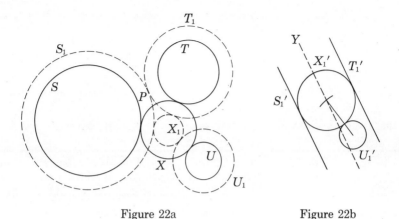

Figure 22a   Figure 22b

separation between the two closest circles (in this case S and T). We also decrease the radius of the required circle, X, by a like amount. The result is illustrated by the dashed circles in the figure. Note that the dashed circles S_1 and T_1 are now tangent. Since this process can be reversed, we are entitled to substitute for the original problem the problem of constructing a circle which is tangent to three given circles, two of which are externally tangent to one another.

We now invert the four dashed circles in Figure 22a, with respect to point P as origin. Figure 22b illustrates the result. Circles S_1 and T_1 become the parallel lines S_1' and T_1'. Circle U_1 becomes circle U_1'. Circle X_1 becomes circle X_1', which is tangent to S_1', T_1', and U_1'. Our problem now is as follows: given two parallel lines, S_1' and T_1', and a circle U_1' between them, we are to construct a circle which is tangent to S_1', T_1', and U_1'. Obviously, the center of X_1' lies somewhere on the line Y, which is parallel to S_1' and T_1', and halfway between them. Its radius is one-half the perpendicular distance between S_1' and T_1'. We note that the distance between the centers of X_1' and U_1' is the sum of their radii. With this distance as radius and with the center of U_1' as center, we describe an arc cutting Y at the center of X_1'. Circle X_1' is now fully determined and can be constructed. We then invert circle X_1' with respect to the original origin, which gives us circle X_1 in Figure 22a. By increasing the radius of circle X_1 by the same amount as the radii of circles S and T were increased, we arrive at circle X, the solution of the problem of Apollonius.

CHAPTER FOUR

Conic Sections

32. Conic sections have been of interest to mathematicians since remote antiquity. A treatise on them was written by Apollonius of Perga more than 2000 years ago. Investigation of their properties is the chief aim of analytic geometry. Although not always recognized, they are the commonest curves in everyday life. They are the shadows of a circular object cast by the sun on a plane surface; the boundary between the bright and dim illumination on a wall provided by a lamp with a shade open at the top; the paths of comets, planets, and satellites, natural or artificial; the cross section of the surface of a liquid in a spinning bowl; the paths of electrons within an atom; the shape of automobile headlight or searchlight reflectors; and the mirrors of reflecting telescopes.

For our purposes, conic sections may be simply defined as the intersections of a circular cone with a plane. A circular cone is defined as a surface generated by a straight line which passes through every point of a circle and through a fixed point not in the plane of the circle. Since the line may be of indefinite length, the cone is actually double, the two halves having a common axis and apex.

There are different types of conic sections, depending on the angle between the plane and the axis of the cone; thus we have the circle, ellipse, parabola, and hyperbola. We must also include in the class of conic sections a single point, a single line, and a pair of lines; for the plane may pass through the apex of the cone without cutting any other portion (giving a point); it may pass through the apex and be tangent to the cone (giving a single line); or it may pass through the apex and cut the cone (giving a pair of lines). In any case, all of these conic sections have many properties in common, as we shall discover in the next chapter.

The various conic sections differ from one another in their metrical properties, with which the usual course in geometry is concerned. Our present interest, however, is in other properties common to all members of the class. These are called *projective* properties. They will be developed in the next chapter.

CHAPTER FIVE

Central Projection

33.   Imagine a configuration in a plane (the picture plane), a point O (the center of projection) outside the plane, and a second plane (the projection plane) arbitrarily placed in space. If straight rays are drawn from O through each point of the figure in the picture plane, each ray will intersect the projection plane in a point, called the projected image of the picture point. The group of points on the projection plane constitutes the projected image of the original configuration. Clearly, the image of a straight line will be a straight line, for the bundle of rays from the center of projection through each point of the original line all lie in a plane. The intersection of this plane with the plane of projection will be a straight line. Thus an original figure consisting of only points and straight lines will project into an image of corresponding points and straight lines. Hence points and straight lines are invariants under projection. However, the magnitudes of angles and of distances between points are not invariants.

Figure 23 illustrates the facts discussed thus far. Clearly, either plane may be regarded as the picture plane, and either figure may be regarded as the projection of the other. The two planes may be on opposite sides of O, or both may be on the same side, as in the figure. Curved lines, in general, project into curves, and the images of tangent curves will be tangent to each other (since they have only one point in common). Thus tangency is another invariant under projection. Such invariants are called *projective properties* of figures. Other projective

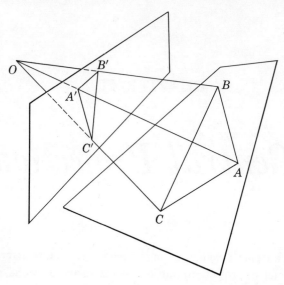

Figure 23

properties are the degree and order of curves. (The degree of a curve is the number of points in which it can be intersected by a straight line; the order is the number of tangents which can be drawn to the curve from a point). Although the projection of a circle is ordinarily not a circle, it is always a curve of second degree; in fact, from our definition of conic sections in Chapter IV, it must be a circle, an ellipse, a parabola, or a hyperbola. (A circle may be projected into a point, which may be considered as a null circle. Strictly speaking, a circle cannot be projected into one or two straight lines, although these images may be regarded as the limiting case of a parabola or hyperbola as the projection plane approaches coincidence with a side of the cone or its apex.) In general, the length of line segments and the ratio between two line segments are changed by projection; however, it is a remarkable fact that cross ratio is invariant. For proof of the latter property refer to Figure 24.

34.   Let *ABCD* be four points lying on the straight line *L* and let *O* be the center of projection. Let the plane of the paper be the plane determined by *L* and *O*. On this plane let *L'* be the trace of an arbitrarily

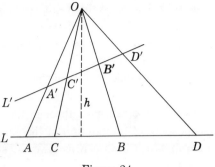

Figure 24

placed projection plane, and let h be the perpendicular height of O above L. Clearly, then, we have the following equations:

a. Area of triangle $OCA = \frac{1}{2}h \times CA = \frac{1}{2}OA \times OC \sin COA$.
b. Area of triangle $OCB = \frac{1}{2}h \times CB = \frac{1}{2}OC \times OB \sin COB$.
c. Area of triangle $ODA = \frac{1}{2}h \times DA = \frac{1}{2}OA \times OD \sin DOA$.
d. Area of triangle $ODB = \frac{1}{2}h \times DB = \frac{1}{2}OD \times OB \sin DOB$.

e. Dividing a by b, $\dfrac{CA}{CB} = \dfrac{OA \times \sin COA}{OB \times \sin COB}$.

f. Dividing c by d, $\dfrac{DA}{DB} = \dfrac{OA \times \sin DOA}{OB \times \sin DOB}$.

g. Dividing e by f, $\dfrac{\frac{CA}{CB}}{\frac{DA}{DB}} = \dfrac{\frac{\sin COA}{\sin COB}}{\frac{\sin DOA}{\sin DOB}}$.

The sense of angles being taken into account, equation g states that the cross ratio $(ABCD)$ depends only on the angles at O. Since these angles are the same for the range on L' as for the range on L, we see that $(A'B'C'D') = (ABCD)$; i.e., the cross ratio of a range of four points is invariant under projection. This projective property of cross ratio is of great importance in projective geometry. The present scope is too limited for a comprehensive development of the subject, but a few interesting applications will be discussed below.

35. First, note from Figure 24 that (*ABCD*), being a function of the angles of the pencil, can equally designate the cross ratio of the range or of the pencil. The cross ratio of the pencil is usually denoted by (*O − ABCD*). Also, note that the value of the cross ratio of the range on the transversal *L'* is independent of the position of the transversal (since the angles of the pencil are fixed). It is also true that the cross ratio of a pencil, whose rays pass through the four points of a given range, is independent of the position of the pencil. This is illustrated by Figure 25, in which both pencils have the same cross ratio, namely that of the range *ABCD*.

36. Now refer to Figure 26a, which shows two pencils radiating from points *O* and *O'* on a circle, and having in common four other points *A*, *B*, *C*, and *D* on the circle. From elementary geometry we know that the corresponding angles of the two pencils are equal (being measured by the same arcs). Therefore the two pencils *O − ABCD* and *O' − ABCD* have the same cross ratio. This establishes the following theorem: the cross ratio of a pencil formed by lines joining four fixed points and one variable point on a circle is independent of the position of the variable point. Now, let us project Figure 26a onto another plane. Figure 26b is the resulting image. The circle projects into another conic (in this case an ellipse). The six points *O*, *O'*, *A*, *B*, *C*, and *D* project into corresponding points on the ellipse. Similarly, the two pencils inscribed

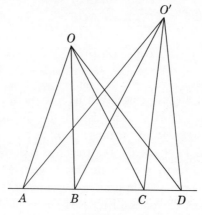

Figure 25

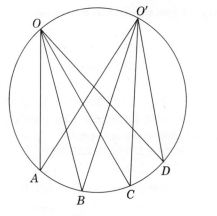

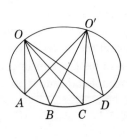

Figure 26a   Figure 26b

in the ellipse correspond to the two original pencils. Now, from the projective property of cross ratio, the two pencils in the ellipse have the same cross ratio, which is equal to the cross ratio of the two original pencils. This leads to the following theorem: the cross ratio of a pencil formed by lines joining four fixed points and one variable point on a conic is independent of the position of the variable point.

This remarkable result is an excellent example of the value of a projective transformation. A theorem regarding conics has been deduced from a simpler one regarding a circle. What we have proved with regard to a circle is equally true with respect to an ellipse, a parabola, a hyperbola, or two straight lines.

37. Configurations consisting of points and their interconnecting lines are closely allied to configurations made up of straight lines and their points of intersection. For each figure of one type there is a corresponding figure of the other type, called its *dual*. We have already encountered a pair of such dual configurations in Figures 24 and 25, discussed in Articles 34 and 35. We shall meet more as we proceed, notably in the theorems of Pascal and Brianchon (Chapter VI).

38. In Article 36 it was proved that the cross ratio of a pencil of four lines joining four fixed points with one variable point on a conic

is constant. We shall now prove the dual theorem: the cross ratio of the range of four points in which a variable tangent intersects four fixed tangents to a conic is independent of the position of the variable tangent. First, refer to Figure 27a, representing a circle with two fixed tangents, MP and MQ, and a variable tangent, AB. Note that angle AOB, subtended at the center of the circle by points A and B, in which the fixed and variable tangents intersect, is constant, regardless of the position of the variable tangent. This becomes clear if we note that

$$\text{angle } AOB = \text{angle } AOR + \text{angle } ROB = \tfrac{1}{2} \text{ angle } POR + \tfrac{1}{2} \text{ angle } ROQ$$
$$= \tfrac{1}{2} \text{ angle } (POR + ROQ)$$
$$= \tfrac{1}{2} \text{ angle } POQ \text{ (a constant).}$$

Now refer to Figure 27b. By the principle just proved, angle MON, subtended at the center of the circle by the points of intersection, M and N, of the variable tangent, MQ, with the two fixed tangents, MA and NB, is constant for all positions of MQ. Similarly, angles NOP and POQ

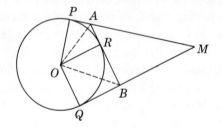

Figure 27a

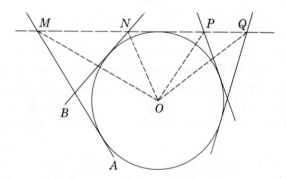

Figure 27b

are constant. Thus the cross ratio of the pencil $O - MNPQ$ (being a function of these angles) and that of the range $MNPQ$ is constant. Now, by a projection, Figure 27b can be represented as four fixed tangents and one variable tangent to any of the other conic sections, and the cross ratio of the range $MNPQ$ will remain constant, regardless of the position of the variable tangent. Thus the theorem of this article is proved.

39.   It will be recalled from our study of circular inversion that when a figure is inverted, the resulting figure is simplified by a suitable choice of the center of inversion. This has its counterpart in a projective transformation, in that the resulting figure is simplified by a suitable choice of a center of projection and the placement of the projection plane. Refer to Figure 28. Each ray from point O through a point in plane P intersects plane S in a finite point. Now assume that point O and plane P are held fixed and that plane S is moved so that it is parallel to ray OD. Figure 29 shows the result. Ray OD can no longer intersect plane S in a finite point. Point D projects into a point at infinity in plane S. Therefore the projections of lines AD and CD in plane P become parallel lines in plane S (they intersect in infinity). Now, since plane S may be placed so that it is parallel to *two* rays from O, it is

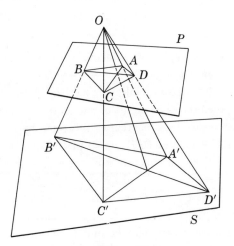

Figure 28

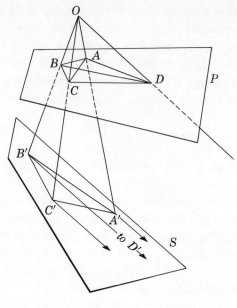

Figure 29

possible to project to infinity any two points of a figure. Lines intersecting in these points in the original figure become sets of parallel lines
after projection. The line joining the two points in the original figure
is projected into the line at infinity.

40.   Let us now apply this principle to prove a famous theorem
about two triangles (Desargues's Theorem), which reads as follows: if
two triangles are so placed that lines joining their corresponding vertices
are concurrent, then the three points of intersection of their corresponding sides are collinear. This theorem is illustrated by Figure 30a. Here
the two triangles, *ABC* and *DEF*, are so placed that the joins of their
corresponding vertices are concurrent at point *G*. Corresponding sides
AB and *ED* intersect at *P*, *BC* and *EF* at *Q*, and *AC* and *DF* at *R*. It is
to be proved that *P*, *Q*, and *R* are collinear. In the figure the two triangles are shown in the same plane. It is a remarkable fact that the
theorem is true when the triangles lie in different planes. The proof for
the latter case is simple, but we shall omit it. Figure 30b represents the

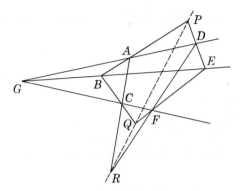

Figure 30a

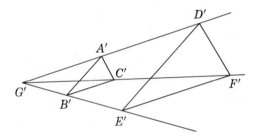

Figure 30b

projection of Figure 30a from a point O, not in the plane of the figure (and not shown) onto a plane parallel to plane OPQ. The images of points P and Q do not appear in Figure 30b, since they have receded to infinity; hence the lines AB and ED have become the parallel lines $A'B'$ and $E'D'$. Similarly, lines BC and EF have become the parallel lines $B'C'$ and $E'F'$. Now, from the similarity of triangles $G'B'A'$ and $G'E'D'$, we know that $G'A'/G'D' = G'B'/G'E'$. Also, from the similarity of triangles $G'B'C'$ and $G'E'F'$, we know that $G'B'/G'E' = G'C'/G'F'$. Therefore $G'A'/G'D' = G'C'/G'F'$, and $A'C'$ is parallel to $D'F'$. This means that the image of point R, the intersection of AC and DF (in Figure 30a), has receded to infinity (in Figure 30b). Thus the three points P, Q, and R are collinear, since their projections are collinear at infinity. (We recall that all infinite points in the plane lie on the line at infinity.) This proves the theorem. The converse theorem is also true: if two triangles are so placed that the intersections of their corresponding sides are collinear, then the joins of their corresponding vertices are concurrent. The proof is left as an exercise for the reader.

41. We have seen previously how the principles of circular inversion may be employed to transform theorems of elementary geometry into other theorems. Similarly, transformations may be performed by central projection, and deductions may be made concerning the transformed figure by observing the invariants. The field of conic sections is a most fruitful one because of the projective relationship among the several forms of the conics. We have seen that when a circular cone is intersected by any number of planes, a configuration on any one plane is projected into a corresponding configuration on each of the other planes, the apex of the cone being the center of projection. Consequently, all of the configurations are projectively equivalent, and the projective properties of one are common to all. Thus many theorems involving the ellipse, parabola, and hyperbola may be inferred from theorems concerning the circle.

42. Projective methods enable us to derive the remarkable properties of the *complete quadrilateral*, a figure composed of four straight lines and their six intersections. In Figure 31a, A, B, C, D, E, and F are the six vertices of the complete quadrilateral formed by the four lines AF, AE, BE, and DF. The dashed lines AC, DB, and EF are called the diagonals. They are drawn between vertices which do not lie on the same side. The intersections of the diagonals are marked by points G, H, and J. Now consider the range $EFHJ$. Note that this range is the projection, from point C, of the range $BDGJ$ onto line EJ. Note also that the same range, $EFHJ$, is also projected from point A onto line DJ, giving the corresponding range $DBGJ$. Now, because of the invariance of cross ratio under projection, the cross ratios of these three ranges are equal; i.e., $(EFHJ) = (BDGJ) = (DBGJ) = k$. Observe that $(BDGJ) = 1/(DBGJ)$. (We learned in Article 12 that a reversal in the order of the first two points of a four-point range results in the reciprocal of the cross ratio). Consequently, in this case $k = 1/k$, or $k^2 = 1$. Therefore $k = \pm 1$. We select the negative value since, in the range

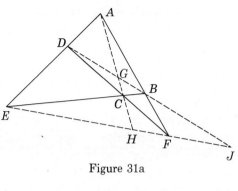

Figure 31a

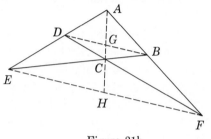

Figure 31b

EFHJ, *H* divides segment *EF* internally and *J* divides it externally. We recall that when $k = -1$, the range is harmonic. Thus the two ranges, on *EJ* and *DJ*, are harmonic. This leads to the following theorem: in a complete quadrilateral two of the diagonals divide harmonically the segment between the vertices on the third diagonal; i.e., the segment is divided internally and externally in the same ratio. The four points on the third diagonal form a harmonic range.

43. Figure 31b is a projection of Figure 31a onto a plane parallel to the ray from the center of projection (not shown) through the point *J*. Thus the image of point *J* lies at infinity. However, the cross ratio $(EFHJ) = (BDGJ) = -1$ is invariant under the projection. Hence, in Figure 31b, points *G* and *H* are midpoints of the diagonals *DB* and *EF*, respectively. Therefore we have the theorem: in a complete quadrilateral, if two of the diagonals are parallel, then the third diagonal bisects both of them.

44. A theorem attributed to Pappus of Alexandria (fourth century A.D.) has to do with six points lying alternately on two straight lines and with the hexagon formed by interconnecting the points. The hexagon is not of the usual convex type. It has re-entrant angles, and one or more of the sides may intersect more than two others. Opposite sides are considered to be the first and fourth, second and fifth, and third and sixth, taken in consecutive order. The theorem states that in such a figure the three points of intersection of opposite sides (extended, if necessary) are collinear. The theorem is illustrated by Figure 32a, in which the hexagon $ABCDEF$ is inscribed on the lines $X - X$ and $Y - Y$. The three points of intersection, R, S, and T, of the opposite sides lie on the line $L - L$.

This theorem is simply proved by projecting the figure, from a point outside the plane, onto a plane parallel to the rays from the center of projection through two of the points of intersection of opposite sides of the hexagon. Figure 32b is the resulting image of such a projection onto a plane parallel to the rays through points R and S. These points project to infinity; consequently, in Figure 32b, the sides $A'B'$ and $D'E'$ are parallel, as are also sides $B'C'$ and $E'F'$. It is to be proved that sides $C'D'$ and $A'F'$ are also parallel. In the figure triangles $G'B'A'$ and $G'D'E'$ are similar; hence $G'A'/G'E' = G'B'/G'D'$. Similarly, since triangles $G'B'C'$ and $G'E'F'$ are also similar, $G'F'/G'B' = G'E'/G'C'$. Therefore $G'F'/G'A' = G'D'/G'C'$. This proves that triangles $G'C'D'$ and $G'A'F'$ are similar. Accordingly, $C'D'$ and $A'F'$ are parallel, and their point of intersection (the image of T) also lies at infinity. Thus the images of R, S, and T are collinear at infinity, which proves the theorem.

It is curious that the Theorem of Pappus is a special case of a more general theorem (Pascal's Theorem) which was not discovered until thirteen centuries later. Pascal's Theorem will be studied in Chapter VI.

We next turn to an interesting and useful pair of theorems.

45. Refer to Figure 33. If two pencils, $O - ABCD$ and $O' - A'B'C'D'$, have the same cross ratio and have a corresponding ray in common, then the intersections of the other three pairs of corresponding rays are collinear. Let the straight line joining b and c meet OA in a, and let the points in which it meets OD and $O'D'$ be called e

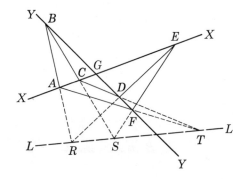

Figure 32a

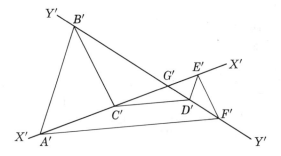

Figure 32b

and e', respectively. Now, evidently $(abce) = (abce')$; but this can be true only if e and e' coincide in point d, the intersection of OD and $O'D'$. Therefore a, b, c, and d are in a straight line.

46. The dual of the theorem in Article 45 reads as follows: if two ranges of four points A, B, C, D and A', B', C', and D' have the same cross ratio and have a corresponding point in common, then the straight lines joining the other three pairs of corresponding points are concurrent. Refer to Figure 34. Let O be the point of intersection of lines BB' and CC'. Draw OA and OD', and let the point in which OD' meets AD be called e. Now, evidently $(AB'C'D') = (ABCe)$; but, by hypothesis, $(AB'C'D') = (ABCD)$. Therefore point e must coincide with point D, and the straight line DD' also passes through O.

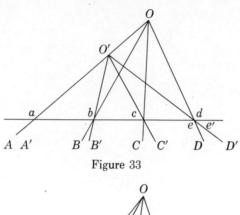

Figure 33

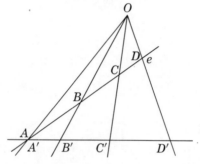

Figure 34

47. The dual theorems of Articles 45 and 46 are useful in proving many other theorems by projective methods. As a case in point, in Article 40 (Figure 30b) Desargues's Theorem was proved by means of similar triangles. We now give proofs of this theorem, and of its converse, by typically projective methods. Refer to Figure 35, where we are given the triangles ABC and DEF, so placed that lines DA, EB, and FC are concurrent at G. We are to prove that points P, Q, and R (the respective intersections of corresponding sides of the two triangles) are collinear. Let AB and DE meet GC in points M and N. We note that the pencil $G - PABC$, intersected by the transversals PM and PN, gives $(PABM) = (PDEN)$. Now note that these two equal cross ratios also belong to two pencils having C and F as vertices, respectively. Hence these two pencils have the same cross ratio. They also have a common ray, CF. Therefore, by Article 45, the intersections of the other three pairs of corresponding rays (points P, Q, and R) are collinear. This proves the theorem.

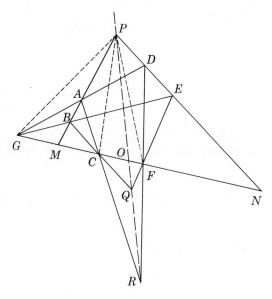

Figure 35

48. The converse of Desargues's Theorem reads: if two triangles are so placed that the points of intersection of corresponding sides are collinear, then the lines joining their corresponding vertices are concurrent. The proof is also illustrated by Figure 35. Let the straight line *PQR* meet line *CF* in point *O*. Note that the two pencils drawn from *C* and *F* through *P*, *O*, *Q*, and *R* have the same cross ratio (Article 35). Now, the pencil from *C* is cut by the transversal *PM* in the range *PMBA*. The pencil from *F* is cut by the transversal *PN* in the range *PNED*. Hence these two ranges have the same cross ratio and, since they have a corresponding point *P* in common, it follows (Article 46) that the lines joining their other three pairs of corresponding points (*NM, EB*, and *DA*) are concurrent. This proves the converse theorem.

CHAPTER SIX

Theorems of Pascal and Brianchon

49. Two of the most important theorems of projective geometry carry the names of their discoverers, Blaise Pascal (1623–1662), a French physicist and mathematician, and Charles Brianchon (1785–1865), another French mathematician. Both theorems are concerned with hexagons and conic sections. Pascal's Theorem states: if a hexagon is inscribed in a conic section, then the intersections of the three pairs of opposite sides are collinear. Brianchon's Theorem reads: if a hexagon is circumscribed about a conic section, then the joins of the three opposite vertices are concurrent.

In Chapter VII, The Principle of Duality, we shall see that each of these theorems is the dual of the other. Pascal discovered his theorem in 1640, when he was only 16 years old. It was not until 1806, 166 years later, that Brianchon announced his theorem as the dual of Pascal's. A proof of each theorem will be given in this chapter.

50. In spite of the concise statements of the theorems, they are very broad in their applications. Both theorems refer to a hexagon; in one, a hexagon is inscribed in a conic section, and in the other, it is circumscribed about a conic section. Because of the projective properties of points, straight lines, and conic sections, either of the configurations may embody any of the various conics. Thus a proof with respect to a circle will suffice, since a circle may be projected into an ellipse, a parabola, or a hyperbola. In this connection we should note that Pascal's Theorem is also true with respect to two straight lines (which are themselves a conic section), as was shown in our discussion of the Theorem of Pappus (Article 44). We should also note that Figures 36a, 36b, and 37, which illustrate Pascal's and Brianchon's Theorems, show the hexagons as convex. The proofs, however, apply equally well to hexagons drawn in any of the sixty different ways in which six points can be interconnected to form the sides, or in which the six sides can intersect to form the vertices.

Our proof of Pascal's Theorem will employ the same device used in proving Desargues's Theorem (Article 40), i.e., a projection of two points of the figure to infinity. This same device, although applicable, will not be used for proving Brianchon's Theorem. The fact that several methods of proof are available is an important feature of both theorems.

51. We proceed now to the proof of Pascal's Theorem. Refer to Figure 36a, where we are given a circle with inscribed hexagon $ABCDEF$. Let AB and ED intersect at P, DC and FA at R, and BC and FE at Q. We are to prove that PQR is a straight line. By a suitable projection, we produce Figure 36b, in which the circle is transformed into another conic (in this case an ellipse) and the images of P and R are projected to infinity. Note that lines $B'A'$, $F'E'$, $F'A'$, and $C'B'$ have been extended to establish the points M and N. In Figure 36b lines NB' and $D'E'$ are parallel, as are lines $C'D'$ and MF'. We need to prove that MC' and NE' are parallel.

The pencils $C' - B'A'F'D'$ and $E' - B'A'F'D'$ have the same cross ratio, being subtended by the same four points on the conic (Article 36). The former pencil is intercepted by the transversal MF', forming the range $MA'F'\infty$, having the cross ratio $F'M/F'A'$. The second pencil is intercepted by the transversal NB', forming the range $B'A'N\infty$, having the cross ratio NB'/NA'. Since these two ranges have the same cross ratio, it follows that

$$\frac{F'M}{F'A'} = \frac{NB'}{NA'}, \text{ or } \frac{F'M - F'A'}{F'A'} = \frac{NB' - NA'}{NA'} = \frac{A'M}{F'A'} = \frac{A'B'}{NA'}.$$

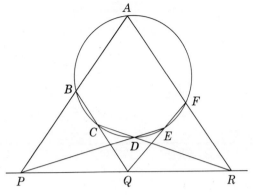

Figure 36a

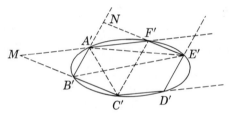

Figure 36b

Hence triangles $NA'F'$ and $MA'B'$ are similar, since they have an angle in common and two sides in proportion. Therefore NE' and $B'C'$ are parallel. Thus, since the images of P, Q, and R are collinear at infinity, these points must be collinear in Figure 36a. This proves the theorem.

52. For the proof of Brianchon's Theorem, refer to Figure 37. Here we have six tangents to a circle, forming the convex hexagon *ABCDEF*. We are to prove that the three dashed lines, joining opposite vertices, intersect in a common point, *O*. For purposes of the proof, sides *AB*, *BC*, *CD*, and *DE* have been extended to establish the points of intersection at *L*, *M*, *N*, and *P*.

Note that we have four tangents, *AB*, *BC*, *CD*, and *EF*, which are cut by a fifth tangent, *ED*, in the points *P*, *N*, *D*, and *E*. The same four tangents are cut by tangent *FA* in points *A*, *L*, *M*, and *F*. Thus we have two ranges having the same cross ratio (Article 38): $(PNDE) = (ALMF)$.

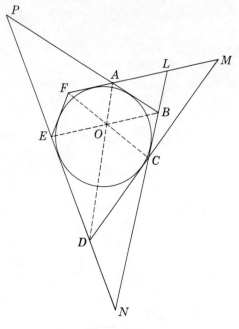

Figure 37

But this implies that the two pencils subtended by these ranges, from points B and C, have the same cross ratio; i.e.,

$$(B - PNDE) = (C - ALMF).$$

(Lines BD and CA are not shown in the figure.) Now, since we have two pencils with the same cross ratio and with a corresponding ray (LN) in common, we know (Article 45) that the points of intersection (A, D, O) of the other three pairs of corresponding rays are collinear. Hence, since point O, the intersection of lines BE and CF, also lies on AD, we have proved that AD, BE, and CF are concurrent.

53.   In the following parallel columns we discuss some interesting corollaries to the two theorems. In each case, the left-hand column applies to Pascal's Theorem and the right-hand column to Brianchon's Theorem.

Corollary 1. If we allow point *D* in Figure 36a to approach point *C* until it coincides with it, side *CD* becomes a tangent at *C*. The theorem will still be true of the resulting pentagon (Figure 38a), if we regard the tangent at *C* as a side of a hexagon having a double vertex. The theorem would then read: if a pentagon is inscribed in a conic, then the intersection of a side with the tangent drawn at the opposite

Corollary 1. If we allow side *DC* in Figure 37 to approach side *CB*, in the limit point *C* will lie on the curve, and tangents *BC* and *CD* will coincide. The theorem will still be true of the resulting pentagon (Figure 38b), if we regard point *C* as a vertex of a hexagon having a doubled side. The theorem would then read: if a pentagon is circumscribed about a conic, then the line joining a ver-

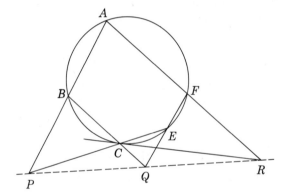

Figure 38a

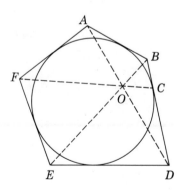

Figure 38b

vertex is collinear with the intersections of the other nonconsecutive sides.

tex and the point of tangency of the opposite side is concurrent with the lines joining the other nonconsecutive vertices.

By the same method, the hexagon may be reduced to a quadrilateral and finally to a triangle; hence we have the following corollaries.

Corollary 2. If a quadrilateral is inscribed in a conic (Figure 39a) and tangents are drawn at two consecutive vertices, then the points of intersection of each of them with

Corollary 2. If a quadrilateral is circumscribed about a conic (Figure 39b), then the lines joining the points of tangency of each of two adjacent sides with the vertex on

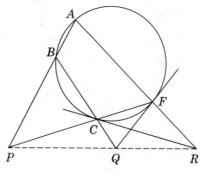

Figure 39a

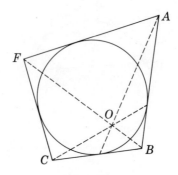

Figure 39b

the side passing through the point of contact of the other are collinear with the point of intersection of the other two sides.

the other side are concurrent with the line joining the other two vertices.

Corollary 3. If a triangle is inscribed in a conic (Figure 40a), then the intersections of each side with a tangent drawn at the opposite vertex are collinear.

Corollary 3. If a triangle is circumscribed about a conic (Figure 40b), then the lines joining the point of tangency of each side with the opposite vertex are concurrent.

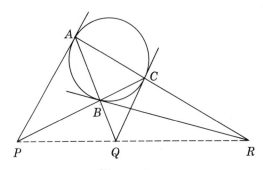

Figure 40a

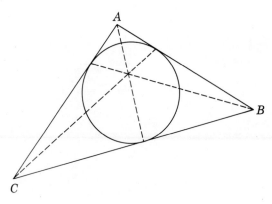

Figure 40b

CHAPTER SEVEN

The Principle of Duality

54.   In the previous chapters we have pointed out the dual nature of certain theorems, e.g., Desargues's Theorem and its converse, and the theorems of Pascal and Brianchon. The reader must have noted others, although attention was not called specifically to them. We showed in Article 35 that if four fixed straight lines, passing through a common point, are intersected by a variable line, the resulting range of four points has a constant cross ratio, regardless of the position of the variable line. In the same article we showed that when four points on a straight line are joined with a variable point, the resulting pencil of four straight lines has a constant cross ratio, regardless of the position of the variable point. These two statements are duals.

55.   The dual nature of geometrical figures is due to the fact that the elements of such figures, the point and the straight line, may each be defined in terms of the other: a straight line is determined by two points, and a point is determined by the intersection of two straight lines. The simplest closed figure is the triangle, which may be regarded as three points interconnected by three lines, or as three lines intersecting in three points. A curve is usually considered as being generated by a moving point, but it can also be generated by a moving line. A curve

65

may therefore be defined either as the *locus* of a point or as the *en* of a line. The generating point lies on its locus; the generating h. tangent to its envelope.

56. Two points on a curve determine a secant, which connects the points. If one point is held fixed and the other allowed to approach it along the curve, the secant approaches and eventually becomes the tangent at the fixed point. Similarly, two tangents to a curve determine a point at their intersection. If one tangent is held fixed and the other allowed to approach it along the curve, their point of intersection approaches and eventually becomes the point of tangency of the fixed tangent. Thus a point on a curve and a tangent to a curve are duals. The curve itself is its own dual.

Collinearity is the dual of *concurrence*. Concurrent lines form a pencil through a point. The dual figure is a range of points on a straight line. For convenience in translating a configuration into its dual, the terms *meet* and *join* are sometimes used as nouns. The meet of two lines is their point of intersection; the join of two points is the unlimited line connecting them.

57. Following is a vocabulary of duals:

A point on a line	A line through a point
The join of two points	The meet of two lines
A point on a curve	A tangent to a curve
A secant to a curve	The meet of two tangents to a curve
Locus of a point	Envelope of a line
A range of points	A pencil of lines
The sides of a polygon	The vertices of a polygon
Cross ratio of a range	Cross ratio of a pencil

58. Two theorems are duals when one becomes the other by replacing each element and operation by its dual. A distinctive feature of

ve geometry is that each of its theorems has its dual. As previously noted, Desargues's Theorem and its converse, and the theorems
of Pascal and Brianchon are duals.

In the following chapter we shall develop a method of transforming
a configuration into its dual.

CHAPTER EIGHT

Polar Reciprocation

59. A third type of transformation, polar reciprocation, differs from circular inversion and central projection in that points and lines are transformed, respectively, into lines and points. A curve generated by a moving point becomes a curve generated by a moving line. A point on a curve is transformed into a tangent to a curve. Points lying on a straight line become lines passing through a common point. A comprehensive treatment of the subject is beyond the scope of the present book, since the subject is largely concerned with the properties of conic sections and therefore requires a knowledge of analytic geometry. However, a descriptive treatment will reveal much that is of interest.

Polar reciprocation is concerned with *poles* and *polars*. A pole is a point; a polar is a straight line. To establish the correspondence between the two, a conic of reference is required, called the *auxiliary conic*. For the present we shall use a circle as the auxiliary conic. Refer to Figure 41,

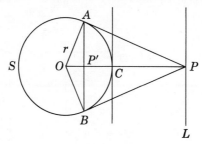

Figure 41

69

where S is the auxiliary circle and P is a point lying outside the circle. The polar of point P is defined as the line AB, joining the points where tangents from P touch the circle. (We shall shortly extend this definition to include the cases where P is on or inside the circle.) P is called the pole of the line AB. Clearly, AB is perpendicular to OP.

Note that AB intersects OP in the point P' and also that triangles $AP'O$ and OAP are similar. Therefore $OP'/r = r/OP$, or $OP \times OP' = r^2$. We see, therefore, that P' is the inverse of P, with respect to circle S. We can now revise our definition of pole and polar to include the condition that P lies inside the circle, as follows: the polar of a point with respect to a circle is the straight line through the inverse of the point, drawn perpendicular to the line joining the point with the center of the circle. Accordingly, not only is AB the polar of P, but line L is the polar of P'. Each point is the pole of its respective polar. Note that if the point lies on the auxiliary circle, its polar is the tangent at the point. This is the only case in which a point lies on its own polar. As a point approaches the center of the circle, its polar recedes until, at the limit when the point coincides with the center, it becomes the line at infinity. Thus the center of the circle and the line at infinity are, respectively, pole and polar; and the pole of a line through the center is a point at infinity in the direction perpendicular to the line.

60.   Now let us investigate the polars of points which lie on a straight line. Refer to Figure 42, where we are given line L and auxiliary

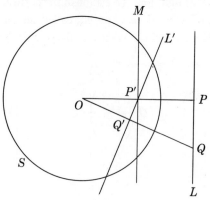

Figure 42

circle S. Let P be the foot of a perpendicular from O to line L. Let P' be the inverse of P. Then line M, drawn through P' and perpendicular to OP, is the polar of P. Also, line L is the polar of P'. Take any point Q on L and let Q' be its inverse. Draw line L', connecting P' and Q'. Now, we know that $OP \times OP' = OQ \times OQ'$. Thus we have two triangles, OPQ and $OP'Q'$, with an angle in common and the sides including the angle in proportion. Therefore triangles OPQ and $OP'Q'$ are similar. Angle $OQ'P'$, being equal to angle OPQ (a right angle), is therefore a right angle. Thus line L' is the polar of Q. (It is perpendicular to OQ and passes through the inverse of Q.) We conclude, then, that as Q moves on L, its polar always passes through the fixed point P', the pole of L. By similar but reverse reasoning, we can show that the poles of all lines passing through P' lie on line L. Accordingly, we can state that the polars of collinear points are concurrent, and that the poles of concurrent lines are collinear.

61. In Figure 43 L is the polar of P. PNM is an arbitrary secant drawn through P, cutting the circle in M and N. Let the tangents at M and N intersect at T. Now T must lie on L, for T is the pole of TNM, TM is the polar of M, and TN is the polar of N. By the principle established in the previous article, the polars of the collinear points P, N, and

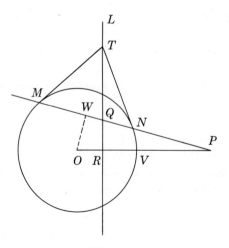

Figure 43

M must be concurrent at T, the pole of PM. We can now state the following theorem: if a secant is drawn to the auxiliary circle through a fixed point in the plane, then tangents at the points where the secant meets the circle will intersect on the polar of the fixed point.

62.   Again referring to Figure 43, note that line PO cuts the circle at V and cuts line L at R. W is the foot of a perpendicular from O to PM. Obviously, W is the midpoint of MN. We shall now prove that points M, N, Q, and P constitute a harmonic range, i.e., that $(MNPQ) = -1$. It will be sufficient to prove that $WQ \times WP = WN^2$ (Article 10). Clearly, $WQ \times WP = WP(WP - QP) = WP^2 - WP \times QP$. Now since the angles at W and R are right angles, points O, W, Q, and R all lie on a circle having OQ as diameter. Consequently, since PW and PO are secants to this circle, $WP \times QP = OP \times RP$. Therefore

$$WQ \times WP = WP^2 - OP \times RP = WP^2 - OP(OP - OR)$$
$$= WP^2 - OP^2 + OP \times OR.$$

Now, $OP \times OR = OV^2$ (since L is the polar of P). Hence

$$WQ \times WP = OV^2 - OW^2 = ON^2 - OW^2 = WN^2.$$

Therefore $(MNPQ) = -1$.

The foregoing can be expressed as follows: if a secant is drawn to a circle from any point in its plane, then the secant is divided harmonically by the circle, the point, and the polar of the point with respect to the circle.

The converse is also true: if a secant to a circle is drawn through a fixed point, then the harmonic conjugate of the point, with respect to the points in which the secant intersects the circle, lies on the polar of the point, for there can be only one harmonic conjugate to a given point with respect to a given line segment.

63.   Again referring to Figure 43, imagine the secant PM as swinging about point P. Obviously, point Q will always lie on line L, the polar

of P. The tangents at M and N will always intersect on L (Article 61), and in the limit, when the secant becomes tangent to the auxiliary circle, point Q will become the point of tangency through which the polar L will pass. This is in accord with the original definition of a polar, as given in Article 59, namely that the polar of a point with respect to a circle is the straight line joining the points of contact of tangents drawn to the auxiliary circle from the fixed point, i.e., provided the point is outside the circle.

64.   In Figure 44a two secants pass through the fixed point P and intersect the auxiliary circle in points R, Q and S, T, respectively. If the chords RT, QS, RS, and QT are drawn, their points of intersection, M and N, will lie on the polar of P. To prove this, note that lines MT, MS, QT, and RS form a complete quadrilateral, of which QR, ST, and MN are the three diagonals. We know from Article 42 that each diagonal is divided harmonically by the other two. Accordingly, the two ranges $TSWP$ and $RQVP$ are harmonic. Points V and W, being harmonic conjugates to P, with respect to segments RQ and ST, must lie on the polar of P (by the converse theorem of Article 62). Consequently, since these two points lie on the line MN, that line is the polar of P.

Figure 44b illustrates the foregoing proof for the case in which P lies inside the circle. The proof is also valid, word for word, for this case.

65.   In Figures 44a and 44b dashed lines are shown connecting points M, P and P, N. They are, respectively, the polars of the points N and M. This is apparent if we note that SR and QT are secants through N. Their four points of intersection with the auxiliary circle are S, R, Q, and T. Hence, by the theorem of the preceding article, the intersections of chords QR and ST (point P) and of SQ and TR (point M) lie on the polar of N. Also, lines SQ and TR are secants through M. Accordingly, by similar reasoning, PN is the polar of M. Note that in the triangle PMN each vertex is the pole of the opposite side. Such a triangle is called *self-polar*.

66.   Up to this point poles and polars have been related to each other by reference to an auxiliary circle. It is a remarkable fact that,

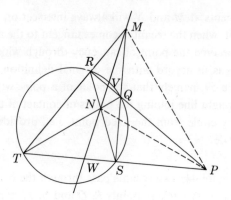

Figure 44a

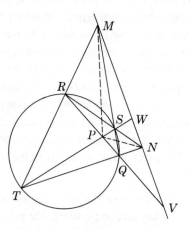

Figure 44b

with one exception, every characteristic of poles and polars thus far discussed is true when the auxiliary circle is replaced by an auxiliary conic. The exception is the definition of pole and polar, given in Article 59, namely that the polar of a point is the straight line through the inverse of the point, drawn perpendicular to the line joining the point with the center of the auxiliary circle. This definition does not apply when an auxiliary conic is used. The definition given in Article 64, however, is true if the word "circle" is replaced by "conic." It would then read: the polar of a point with respect to an auxiliary conic is the locus of the harmonic conjugate of the point with respect to the segment in which any secant through the point is cut by the conic. The validity of the new definition can be proved by projecting Figures 44a and 44b, from a point outside their planes, onto another plane. Each of the points and lines of these figures will project into corresponding points and lines. The auxiliary circle will project into a conic. Also, the harmonic ranges $RQVP$ and $TSWP$ will become corresponding harmonic ranges. Accordingly, the line $MVNW$, which in the original figure is the polar of P, will become a corresponding line, the polar of the image of P, with respect to the conic.

A similar projection of Figure 43 (omitting line OW) will transform the auxiliary circle into a conic, of which the image of line PM will be a secant. The two tangents MT and NT will become tangents to the conic at the points corresponding to M and N, and the image of Q will be the harmonic conjugate of the image of P, with respect to the segment intercepted by the conic (since cross ratio is invariant under projection). Therefore the image of L, the polar of P, will be a straight line, the polar of the image of P.

67. Thus, whether the auxiliary curve be a circle, an ellipse, a parabola, or a hyperbola, the following will summarize the facts regarding the polar of a point in its plane:

a. The polar is a straight line.
b. When the point lies outside the conic, its polar is the chord of contact of the two tangents from the point.
c. If a secant is drawn through the point, tangents at the two points where the secant intersects the conic will intersect on the polar of the point.
d. When a secant through a point cuts the conic, the segment formed by the two points of intersection is divided harmonically by the point and the point in which the polar cuts the secant.
e. The intersections with a conic of two secants drawn through a point outline a quadrilateral, inscribed in the conic, of which the intersections of a pair of opposite sides and of a pair of diagonals each lie on the polar of the point (Figures 44a and 44b).

68.   Referring again to Figures 44a and 44b, assume that the secant *PR* is held fixed and that secant *PT* is allowed to approach indefinitely close to *PR*. In the limit, lines *RT* and *QS* will become tangents at points *R* and *Q*, and they will intersect on *MN*. This is another proof of Fact c of the previous article, namely that tangents at the points where a secant through a given point intersects the auxiliary conic will intersect on the polar of the point.

69.   Assume a curve *S* in the plane of an auxiliary conic. To each point of the curve will correspond a straight line, the polar of the point. Now imagine that the point moves and traces out the curve. Its polar will also move and envelop another curve, *S'*, to which the polars will be tangent. *S'* is called the polar reciprocal of *S*. Next consider two points on *S* and the two corresponding tangents to *S'*. To the line connecting the two points on *S* will correspond the point of intersection of the two tangents to *S'*, the pole of that line. This follows from the theorem of Article 60, which states that the polars of points on a straight line intersect at the pole of that line. In the limit, when the two points on *S* are made to coincide, the line connecting them becomes the tangent to *S* at the double point. The point of intersection of the corresponding tangents to *S'* becomes a point lying on *S'*. Thus there is established a reciprocal relationship between the points and tangents of *S* and the tangents and points of *S'*, respectively. Each of the curves is the reciprocal of the other.

70.   The process of transforming one configuration into another by this means is called *polar reciprocation*. Although its greatest value is in its application to conic sections, and beyond the present scope, it is possible to give a few relatively simple illustrations. Before doing so, it is necessary to point out another characteristic of poles and polars when the auxiliary conic is a circle. Given two straight lines and their poles, the poles will lie on perpendiculars drawn to the lines from the center of the auxiliary circle. We know from elementary geometry that the angle between these perpendiculars is equal to the angle between the given lines. With this in mind, let us reciprocate the theorem that the three altitudes of a triangle intersect in a point. Refer to Figure 45. Here S is the auxiliary circle with center at O. The three altitudes of triangle ABC intersect at X. Triangle $A'B'C'$ is the reciprocal of triangle ABC, $B'C'$ being the polar of A, $A'B'$ the polar of C, and $A'C'$ the polar of B. Now, the pole of the altitude AP is a point D, lying on $B'C'$, the polar of A. (The poles of concurrent lines AP, AC, and AB are collinear with the polar of A, by the theorem of Article 60.) Similarly, the poles of altitudes BQ and CR are the points E and F, lying respectively on $A'C'$ and $A'B'$. Also, A' is the pole of BC, B' the pole of AC, and C' the pole

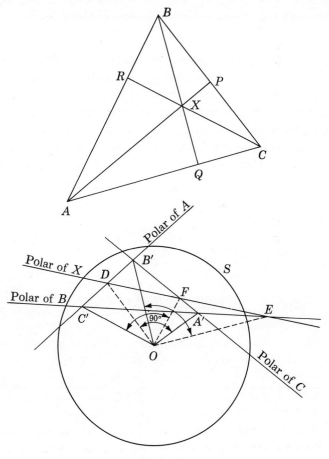

Figure 45

of *AB*. Since the three altitudes of triangle *ABC* are concurrent, their poles, points *D*, *E*, and *F*, are collinear and lie on the polar of *X*. Now, if we join center *O* with the vertices of triangle *A'B'C'* and with the three points *D*, *E*, and *F*, then the angles *A'OD*, *B'OE*, and *C'OF* will each be right angles, since they are subtended at the center of the auxiliary circle by the poles of lines which are perpendicular to one another (the altitudes and corresponding sides of triangle *ABC*). Accordingly, we may deduce the following theorem: if straight lines are drawn from the vertices of a triangle to a point in its plane, then other lines through the point drawn perpendicular to these lines will intersect the sides opposite the respective vertices in three collinear points.

71.   As a final illustration of reciprocation, we shall show that the theorems of Pascal and Brianchon are mutually reciprocal. Refer to Figure 46. Here the hexagon inscribed in the circle illustrates Pascal's Theorem, and the circumscribed hexagon illustrates Brianchon's Theorem. The circle is to be regarded as the auxiliary circle. Note that the sides of the Brianchon hexagon are tangents at the vertices of the inscribed figure. These Brianchon sides are therefore the polars of the

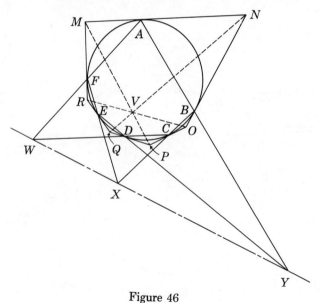

Figure 46

Pascal vertices. (The polar of a point on the auxiliary circle is the tangent at that point.) Each figure is thus the reciprocal of the other. Note that each of the three collinear Pascal points (W, X, and Y) is the pole of the three Brianchon lines. Now, since this figure may be projected onto another plane, the auxiliary conic may be transformed into any of the other conics. All of the points and lines of the original figure will project into points and lines, the latter having corresponding points of tangency with the auxiliary conic. The properties of concurrence of lines and collinearity of points will be preserved. Hence either theorem may be inferred from the other.

Exercises

The student is urged to do the following exercises. By doing them he will not only improve his understanding of the subjects, but he will also acquire a facility in the application of the principles of geometrical transformations which will enable him to appreciate their fundamental nature and beauty. If he can find more than one method of solving the problems, he should apply the methods to obtain alternative solutions. In performing constructions, a sharp pencil, straightedge, and compasses should be used. This is especially important in performing the inversions called for in the exercises for Chapter III.

CHAPTER ONE

1. Show that the power of a point with respect to a circle is not only the square of the tangent from the point (or the negative of the square of one-half the minimum chord through the point), but also the product of the segments into which the point divides that portion lying within the circle of a secant through the point.

2. What is the power of the center of a circle? Of a point on its circumference? What limit does the power of a point within a circle approach when the radius increases without limit?

3. Construct the radical axis of two circles with centers 2 inches apart, using a radius of $1\frac{1}{2}$ inches for one circle and a radius of $\frac{3}{4}$ inch for the other. Add two more circles to the figure which are members of the same coaxal family.

4. Construct the radical axis of two circles with centers 3 inches apart, each circle having a radius of 1 inch. Add several more circles to this family, using a graphical method. Check the results by computation.

5. Construct the radical axis of two circles with centers 2 inches apart, using a radius of $1\frac{1}{2}$ inches for one circle and a radius of $\frac{1}{2}$ inch for the other. Add several more circles to the family.

6. Construct the radical axis of two circles with centers 2 inches apart, using a radius of 1 inch for one circle and a radius of $\frac{1}{2}$ inch for the other. Add several more circles to the family and find the two limiting points.

7. Where are the limiting points of the family of Exercise 5?

8. Construct a system of two conjugate families of coaxal circles.

9. Given a straight line and a point not incident with it. Considering the line as a circle of infinite radius and the point as a circle of zero radius, where is the radical axis? Add another circle to this family.

10. Given two nonintersecting circles with different radii. Does the point of intersection of their internal common tangents lie on their radical axis?

11. Construct two concentric circles and two straight lines passing through their center. Add one more member to each of the conjugate families of coaxal circles.

12. If one point of intersection of two intersecting circles is held fixed and the radii of both circles are allowed to increase without limit, what becomes of the other point of intersection?

13. The center of a system of concentric circles is one of the limiting points of the family. Where is the other?

14. Construct three nonintersecting circles of different radii and locate their radical center.

15. Construct three circles. Let the first and second intersect; also let the second and third intersect, but not the first and third. Find the radical center.

CHAPTER TWO

1. Given a range of four points, A, B, C, and D. B is $\frac{1}{2}$ inch to the right of A; C is $\frac{1}{2}$ inch to the right of B; D is 1 inch to the right of C. What is the value of the cross ratio $(ABCD)$?

2. If $(ABCD) = k$, prove that $(DBCA) = 1 - k$. (Note that the first and last points are interchanged.)

3. If $(ABCD) = k$, prove that $(ACBD) = 1/k$. (Note that the second and third points are interchanged.)

4. If $(ABCD) = k$, prove that $(ABDC) = 1/k$. (Note that the third and fourth points are interchanged.)

5. If $(ABCD) = k$, prove that $(ACDB) = 1/(1 - k.)$

6. On the basis of your experience with Exercises 3, 4, and 5, do you see a quick method of determining the value of (*ADCB*)?

CHAPTER THREE

1. Perform the following inversions, using only a pair of compasses. For each construction use a circle with 1 inch radius as the circle of inversion.

a. Invert a point 3 inches from the origin.

b. Invert a point $\frac{3}{4}$ inch from the origin.

c. Invert a point $\frac{1}{4}$ inch from the origin.

d. Draw a vertical line and a horizontal line intersecting it. Label the vertical line "directrix." Label the horizontal line "axis." Place a point on the axis $\frac{1}{2}$ inch to the right of the directrix, and label it *F* (for focus). Plot ten points, five above and five below the axis, each of whose perpendicular distance from the directrix is equal to its distance from the focus (point *F*). Connect the points with a smooth curve. The curve is a parabola. Draw a circle of $\frac{3}{4}$ inch radius, with center at the intersection of the axis and directrix. Invert each point used in plotting the parabola, with respect to the circle. Connect the inverse points with a smooth curve. The curve so drawn is the inverse of a parabola.

e. Using another directrix and axis (at right angles to each other) and a focus on the axis $\frac{1}{2}$ inch from the directrix, trace the parabola plotted for Exercise 1d, making it symmetrical about the axis and cutting the axis halfway between the focus and the directrix. Using the focus as center of inversion and a circle of 1 inch radius as circle of inversion, invert five points on each branch of the parabola. Connect the inverse points with a smooth curve. The result is the inverse of a parabola with respect to its focus.

f. Invert a circle of $\frac{1}{2}$ inch radius passing through the origin.

2. Perform the following constructions, using only a pair of compasses.

a. Construct the midpoint between two given points and on the straight line joining them, but do not draw the line.

b. Draw a circle of 1 inch radius and find its center.

c. Given two points A and B. Construct a point C such that the line joining A and C is perpendicular to the line joining A and B. (Hint: the angle inscribed in a semicircle is a right angle.)

d. Given an equilateral triangle. Using one vertex as the center of inversion, invert the figure. From the known property of the original figure deduce a property of the inverse figure.

e. Given an equilateral triangle 1 inch on a side. Take an origin $\frac{1}{2}$ inch from one of the vertices and invert the figure. Draw an inference from the result.

3. Construct a figure illustrating the following theorem: an angle inscribed in a semicircle is a right angle. Invert the figure and state the inverse theorem.

4. Given a circle of inversion of 1 inch radius. Call the origin O. Draw a straight line through the origin and on it mark points C, B, and D at distances 2 inches, 3 inches, and 6 inches, respectively. Invert the figure and label the inverse points C', B', and D', respectively. What inference can you draw regarding the position of B' relative to C' and D'? (Hint: the cross ratio of a range of four points on a line through the origin is invariant under projection.)

5. Construct a Peaucellier Cell (see Figure 20) out of cardboard or plastic strips, using rivets to connect the links, except the links should be tacked to the drawing board at O and C, and a pencil used to join the links at P'. Operate the linkage to draw the straight line L, and then remove link CP and describe various curves with point P. Observe that P' will draw the inverse curves.

6. Inscribe a quadrilateral in a circle. Invert the following theorem: the opposite angles of such a quadrilateral are either equal or supplementary. (Hint: invert the figure with respect to one of the vertices.)

CHAPTER FIVE

1. Refer to Figure 31a and prove that the diagonal *AH* of the complete quadrilateral is divided harmonically by the diagonals *DJ* and *FJ*.

2. Draw a straight line and mark on it three points *E*, *H*, and *F*, placing *H* between *E* and *F*. Study Figure 31a and devise a method of finding a point *J* on the line such that *H* and *J* divide the segment *EF* internally and externally in the same numerical ratio; in other words, find the harmonic conjugate of *H*. Use only a pencil and straightedge. This construction is significant in that it demonstrates that the concept of harmonic division can be developed by projective methods, i.e., without the use of measurements.

3. Given a straight line *L* on which there is a harmonic range of four points *A*, *B*, *C*, and *D*, arranged in that order. Take a point *O*, not on the line, and draw the rays from *O* to each of the points on *L*. This will produce a harmonic pencil. Cut this pencil with a transversal drawn parallel to the ray *OD*. Label the points *A'*, *B'*, and *C'* where this transversal cuts the rays *OA*, *OB*, and *OC*, respectively. In what ratio does the point *B'* divide the segment *A'C'*? Why?

4. An artist wishes to depict in perspective a scene in which there is a straight railroad track with a line of telegraph poles running parallel to it. All the poles are the same height and are equally spaced. The two rails and the line joining the tops of the poles seem to meet in a point on the horizon. The artist therefore draws a horizontal line representing the horizon and marks that point (the vanishing point) on it. He then holds his drawing sheet in a vertical plane making his horizon line coincide with the actual horizon and his vanishing point with the corresponding point on the horizon. He then draws three straight lines through his vanishing point, representing the two rails and the line of pole tops. On the latter line he marks the position of each pole top by noting where rays from his eye to the pole tops intersect the sheet. After his drawing is completed, the distance between the tops of the first two poles in the foreground is 2 inches, and that between the second and third poles is 1 inch. If his drawing is accurate, what should be the distance between the third and fourth pole tops?

CHAPTER SIX

1. Construct a circle and mark six points on it. Inscribe a hexagon by connecting consecutive points with straight lines. Find the intersections of opposite pairs of sides of the hexagon, and test the truth of Pascal's Theorem by noting whether the three points so found actually lie on a straight line. (Note: the positions of the six vertices of the hexagon may have to be adjusted so that the intersections of opposite sides will lie on the paper.)

2. Using a figure similar to that of Exercise 1, connect the six vertices of the hexagon in a different order and check the truth of Pascal's Theorem.

3. Check the truth of Brianchon's Theorem by drawing six tangents to a circle and connecting opposite intersections of consecutive tangents.

4. Repeat Exercise 3 by connecting opposite intersections of pairs of nonconsecutive tangents.

5. Repeat all of the foregoing exercises using an accurately drawn ellipse instead of a circle.

CHAPTER SEVEN

Write out the Pascal Theorem, and then translate it into its dual theorem by using the vocabulary of dual elements given in Article 57. (Note: the dual of a conic is a conic.)

CHAPTER EIGHT

1.   Given a circle and a point outside of it. Construct the polar of the point. Repeat the construction for a point inside the circle.

2.   Given a circle and a straight line which intersects it. Construct the pole of the line. Repeat the construction using a straight line which does not intersect the circle.

3.   Experiment with different methods of performing the constructions of Exercises 1 and 2.

4.   Given a circle and two intersecting straight lines. Construct the poles of the lines and the polar of their point of intersection.

Suggestions for
Supplementary Reading

Julian Lowell Coolidge, *A History of Geometrical Methods*, New York, Dover, 1963.

Richard Courant and Herbert Robbins, *What Is Mathematics?* New York, Oxford, 1941.

Luigi Cremona, *Elements of Projective Geometry*, New York, Dover, 1960.

C. Godfrey and A. W. Siddons, *Modern Geometry*, Cambridge, Cambridge University Press, 1912.

Roger A. Johnson, *Advanced Euclidean Geometry*, New York, Dover, 1960.

A. N. Kostevskii, *Geometrical Constructions Using Compasses Only*, New York, Blaisdell, 1961.

L. Mascheroni, *La Geometria del Compasso*, Palermo, Reber, 1901.

George Salmon, *A Treatise on Conic Sections*, New York, Longmans, Green, 1911.

Index

(Numbers refer to articles.)

91